The PROVERBS of LEADERSHIP

Principles
for leading your people
to the pinnacle
of greatness

by

STEVENSON WILLIS

PILLAR
PRESS

Published by
PILLAR PRESS
P.O. BOX 50735
NASHVILLE TN 37205

Please contact Special Orders
for additional information:
1-888-228-0549
<info@pillarpress.com>
Or visit us on the web at
www.pillarpress.com

Willis, Stevenson
The Proverbs of Leadership: *Principles for leading your people to the pinnacle of greatness*
(1) Leadership   (2) Inspiration   (3) Network Marketing

ISBN 0-9713484-1-3

Printed in the United States of America

LIMITED EDITION

— ⌘ —

The pathway to success for the journey you have chosen refuses any traveler who attempts to walk alone. If you are to prosper on the road to which you're called you must gather to your caravan a multitude of many.

How then shall you master the mystery of attraction? And what will compel great numbers to join you? The answer shall be found neither in the force of your persuasion nor in the nobleness of your purpose, *but in the level of your ability to relate to others.*

The creator has endowed each soul with potential, and asks of you to see it in whomever you shall meet. With this simple truth the masses will receive you and the cause you've embraced. Without it you will flounder, even with those whom you love. From this day forth you must view every person in only one way: not as they have been or as they are, *but as how they were created to be.*

For when you view your fellow man through the eyes of our maker compassion and humility will flow from your heart.

And many will draw near to discover the source.

— ⌘ —

TABLE of CONTENTS

———— ✑ ————

CHAPTER ONE

— ❧ —

JERUSALEM, 925 B.C.

DARIUS WALKED BRISKLY FROM HIS DWELLING IN THE LOWER quadrant of the city and cautiously made his way toward the palace complex on the hill. The streets of the walled city were essentially deserted as the merchants and traders had closed their shops hours ago. Nonetheless, he kept a wary eye on the shadows, for on this night, like most as of late, a certain eeriness pervaded the air. The king's heir apparent had an ample contingent of spies and Darius was keenly aware that any record of his attendance at the meeting could threaten his life in the days to come. He kept the hood of his cloak pulled over his head and hoped that he had not been followed.

This was the sixth clandestine meeting in the past fortnight to which Darius had been summoned. He and the other men who made up this secret council had, by default, assumed the leadership of the kingdom as Solomon withdrew more and more into himself. They had effectively steered the nation during the past eighteen tumultuous months, but now, several crises had erupted and the perils seemed to worsen by the hour. Alarmed by its tone, he clutched the cryptic note which requested his presence at the palace and pondered the possible reasons for the urgency of its summons.

King Solomon, the revered wise ruler of days gone by, lay on his deathbed and his incoherent ramblings bordered on the blasphemous. Meanwhile his son and would-be successor, Prince Re'boam, was firmly entrenched by the palace door and gleefully awaited the passing. A superstitious lover of pleasure with a council of fools directing his every move, the young prince was barely able to conceal his wicked joy as he waited to seize power once his father was laid to rest.

The normal transition from king to heir would have itself been enough for Darius and the other royal advisors to contend with, but escalating troubles at home and abroad magnified the tension ten-fold. Throughout the kingdom rumors abounded that the prince would soon put to the sword any and all that refused to acknowledge his right to the crown. Beyond the nation's borders yet no less severe, a financial crisis of Solomon's making loomed large and threatened the stability of the entire region. And the lingering effects of the king's diplomatic blunders had increased the probability of war and ground nearly to a halt the nation's trade with its neighbors. Darius increased his pace the last quarter mile to the palace and reflected upon the calamities which had been spawned by the missteps of his king.

The twelve nomadic tribes of Israel had been formed into a fledgling nation nearly seventy five years prior by the sheer determination of Solomon's father, the mighty warrior king David. But now the young nation, which had begun with such promise and potential, teetered on the edge of anarchy due to Solomon's forced labor programs, his burdensome taxation plans of the recent years and the corresponding corruption and decline of his moral example.

It had not always been so, for the people had once held Solomon in the highest regard. His focus and foresight during the building of the great Temple so many years ago had won them to his side, and a sense of national pride was shared by most as monarchs from distant lands journeyed to Jerusalem to pay homage to their king. But as Solomon's ego began to grow in proportion to his prominence among the rulers of the East, he undertook the massive rebuilding of the cities captured by his father David and expected, indeed demanded, his people to pay the way. His subjects, quite naturally, had grown to resent his arrogant quest for glory.

The elders of the twelve tribes, whose power had been greatly diminished over the past decades as the nation evolved into a monarchy, had long recognized King Solomon's loss of touch with the people. They had waited patiently for several years for the right moment to stir the people with the ideas of revolt and a return to the old tribal system, and now the moment seemed right. The multitudes, burdened as they were with the heavy taxes and disillusioned by the abuses of Solomon's monarchial excesses were receptive, yes, even ready to entertain the idea.

How have we come to this? Darius wondered aloud. *In the winter of his life my king has turned away from the wisdom of his youth and my nation draws closer to collapse each day.* The questions and contradictions posed by his king's life had plagued the insightful young man for some time, and as one given to reflection and introspect Darius had determined to discover the answers as to why his king had fallen.

At thirty-five and the youngest member of the council Darius had only vague recollections of the glorious spring and summer of Solomon's reign; yet he knew the history all too well. No man born of the union between man and woman had ever started out with more divine promise and purpose than Solomon, son of David. And yet no man, before or since, had come to the end of his days with a greater sense of dissatisfaction with life or as many questions as to its ultimate meaning.

What separated my king from the source of his wisdom? Darius asked himself as he recounted the king's life. *Surely not lack of achievement, for his accomplishments as architect, poet and judge were unparalleled. Neither could it be for lack of honor, for his influence, wealth and stature were unsurpassed.*

During the first twenty years of his forty year reign the praises of Solomon's leadership echoed throughout the world, and emissaries from kingdoms near and far sat at his feet, spellbound, absorbing the discourse of his vast knowledge. From the days of his youth it was apparent that the spark of the divine had lighted upon Solomon and that he was to be the great leader who would guide his people to the forefront of nations.

How, then, could one divinely blessed with leadership skills beyond compare be led away from the very one who gifted him with greatness? The questions continued to haunt him as he approached the west entrance into the palace.

Darius presented to the sentry at the gate the royal insignia ring which permitted his unquestioned access to the inner wards of the complex. From the sentry's station he was quietly escorted through the outer courtyard to the entrance of the administration wing of the palace. The council elders had made certain that the night sentries were well compensated and therefore, immune to the bribes of Prince Re'boam's spies in their thirst for knowledge of the workings of the council. Consequently, the sentry's official report to his supervisor, completed at the end of his six hour watch, would read that the night had been uneventful with nary a visitor to the west gate of the palace.

The sentry unlatched the twelve-foot tall double doors which led to the great hall of the administration building and quickly closed them as Darius entered the foyer. The perimeter of the courtyard was well lighted with the oil-fed torches and his eyes struggled to adjust to the dimly lit vestibule as the doors shut behind him. He lingered for a moment acclimating to the darkness, then made his way up the grand stone staircase to the council room on the second floor.

Despite his relative youth Darius had been tapped to join this secret council as a result of his abilities to communicate with the spoken word and the quill. While some of the elders may have initially resented his youth he had gradually earned their respect and proved that he belonged.

He was the sixth member of the group to arrive at this meeting; a quick glance around the room told him that elder Baruch, secretary of the treasury, was the only regular not yet present. *He must be preparing last minute details for his presentation* Darius reasoned, then immediately dismissed the matter. Besides, Baruch often arrived late to these sessions, for the issues relating to the treasury were increasingly precarious and usually last on the council's agenda. Anxious to discover the purpose of the meeting, Darius and the other members dispensed with the usual pleasantries and settled in their respective places.

The ornately carved cypress wood conference table was adequately prepared with quill and ink, as well as fresh parchment and papyrus scrolls in anticipation of the directives and edicts which would come forth from the council. General Nebo, the acknowledged leader of the group, wasted no time in bringing the meeting to order. "My friends," he said to Darius and the other members, "the emergency which necessitated this gathering is singular and severe. I shall begin without delay."

The general stood at the head of the table and commanded a presence befitting of his position. A warrior first and foremost, he had risen to prominence many decades earlier by his stirring acts of bravery in battle. A fearless fighter who had little use for politics or those who did, he inspired courage by his confidence and the unyielding force of his will. Yet the lines on his face on this night exhibited concern that the others had never before seen.

"Gentlemen, as you well know, the treasury of our kingdom is dangerously close to depletion." He cleared his throat and hesitated before continuing. "Regrettably, I must tell you that this crisis was made worse by events of earlier today.

"By now you have noticed that elder Baruch is not with us this evening." The normally unshakeable leader of the council motioned to the empty chair to his right and paused to collect his thoughts. "I must sadly inform you that he will not be joining us tonight - or at any time in the future - for earlier this day he was rushed to the royal infirmary after collapsing while at work within his office."

General Nebo and Baruch were the two senior members of the group and had forged a strong friendship over their years together in the king's service. The general had received the news of his friend's collapse nearly six hours earlier, but it was evident that he was still shaken.

"It appears that he will survive, thanks be to God, but

there has been damage within his brain. He no longer has the function of his speech, nor the usage of the right side of his body."

The other council members sat in silence as the news registered. They had known for some time of Baruch's physical ailments, but this news of his collapse was shocking nonetheless.

Baruch was the eldest of the members and the length of his years had begun to show as of late. His mind had remained clear, but the trembling in his hands and the dimming of his eyes had grown progressively worse in recent months. Two years earlier he had made arrangements to return to the village of his youth to live out the remainder of his days, but the leadership crises in the kingdom dictated that he remain at the treasury.

Though at times an obstinate and difficult man, Baruch had a mind for monetary matters like no other. His performance over the past decade, considering the adverse effects of the king's ill-advised withdrawals from the treasury reserves, had been nothing short of miraculous. *It will be difficult to replace this man,* thought Darius, still digesting the news.

General Nebo continued after a moment of silence. "The royal physicians have given us no hope that Baruch will be able to return to his work; therefore, we must prepare immediately to fill his position. On the surface, it would appear that the logical option would be to elevate one of his under secretaries to fill his post."

In truth, however, the council members knew that this was not a feasible solution. While Baruch's two primary assistants were certainly capable bookkeepers and administrators, they had not been prepared to lead on the scale which was now required.

Baruch was a certifiable genius in matters of finance, but had one glaring weakness. Perhaps from a quirk of personality or a demanding sense of perfection, absolute decision making authority within his department - including over matters of relative insignificance - had remained securely vested in him. He could not (or would not) allow his subordinates to handle the difficult, yet necessary tasks which would increase their knowledge and train them for roles in leadership.

In a less turbulent environment the young assistants could be nurtured until they were ready; but not now. The immense and immediate challenges facing the treasury would demand a seasoned leader at the helm with ample experience in commerce and finance. The council would have to look outside its ranks to fill the vacancy. The man elected would find the task daunting indeed.

THE REVENUE INTO THE ROYAL TREASURY was substantial during the early years of King Solomon's rule and was promptly invested into the building and maintenance of his fortified cities and trade routes throughout the kingdom. A significant portion had been invested as well into the building of the great fleet of royal merchant ships which now sailed from the kingdom's port cities on the Mediterranean.

Solomon's treasury soon overflowed with abundance as his burgeoning trade empire generated vast quantities of profits in gold and silver. It was not long, however, before the lavishness of the royal household increased, as did the cumbersome bureaucracy needed to manage it.

In the more recent years the great bureaucracy spawned by the king's excesses consumed more and more of the annual receipts to the point that now, the annual expenditures exceeded the income. Against his advisors objections the king had authorized the withdrawal of the treasury deposits to be used for ordinary maintenance; as these deposits dwindled year after year the kingdom crept closer and closer to the edge of bankruptcy.

Darius had watched this evolution and thought it a sad and perplexing phenomenon: the more gold that came in, the more people were required to manage it, which in turn required more gold, which in turn required more people to manage it. Seemingly overnight Solomon's great empire had evolved into a bloated monster, and the monster now demanded ever-increasing quantities of sustenance on a regular basis.

The kingdom's total revenues for the current year had been greatly reduced due to two factors, each of which hastened the arrival of the fiscal disaster now present. First, under growing threat of revolt by the ten northern tribes, the council had elected to drastically reduce the onerous tax plan previously established by their king. Unfortunately, the operating costs of the kingdom did not decline in the same proportion, as Prince Re'boam had seized control of the administration of the royal household and thus circumvented the council's ability to reduce expenses.

The second and more significant factor which contributed to the treasury's reduced income was the near constant disruption of the region's trade. In times of peace the roads which linked the kingdom's coastal ports with the empires of the East remained open and safe for the unfettered transport of goods. In recent years, however, warring bands of nomads had sensed the weakening of King Solomon's leadership and regularly raided the caravans which traveled on the kingdom's roads. Having suffered heavy losses, the majority of the region's great traders had curtailed their operations and refused to travel their routes for fear of the marauding bandits. Though General Nebo had personally pledged sufficient protection the traders were of no mind to face the danger. Consequently, the flow of levies and taxes into the treasury from these caravans had slowed to a trickle. Decisive action was needed, as less than one year's supply of gold remained in the nation's coffers.

"THERE ARE FEW MEN in all of the kingdom with the necessary expertise in finance to helm the treasury," General Nebo stated as he removed several pieces of papyrus from his leather attaché. "And fewer still with an equal amount of experience in matters of trade and commerce." He paused for a moment as the sheets of papyrus were passed around the table to the other members. "Truth be known, there is one man whose leadership abilities elevate him above all other candidates."

Darius' copy of the papyrus had barely made its way around the table to him when Johan, chief clerk of the council, spoke up. "But what of Prince Re'boam, who is waiting in the wings for Solomon to pass? Will he not be angered by this move?"

General Nebo immediately dismissed the question. "At last check our King Solomon was counted among the living and thus, still on the throne. Our sworn duty is to him and to our country, not to the heir. We must not allow our decisions to be influenced by fear."

Darius glanced at the papyrus and saw that it contained just one name: Efram Ben-Jared, the great merchant trader of Megiddo.

"Forgive me, general," Johan persisted, "but is this not the same Efram Ben-Jared whose father served with distinction in the courts of King David and King Solomon? Have you forgotten that he walked away from a position of some status in this very court to pursue a career as a common peddler of goods?"

"Yes," replied Nebo, "and it would appear that he made the right choice, did he not? For is he not today commonly referred to as the greatest merchant trader from the near to the far east?"

Johan grudgingly conceded the point, but clearly harbored resentment regarding the success of Efram Ben-Jared. He had supervised Ben-Jared at the outset of his apprenticeship over thirty years ago and had tried, in vain, to dissuade him from leaving the court to seek his fortune in commerce. Efram Ben-Jared's ancestors had served as distinguished scribes for many generations, but his heart did not share the passion for the profession as his fathers. He chose to walk away from the security of his position in pursuit of his dream, and Johan, a man of logic and reason, simply could not understand such a seemingly foolish quest.

"Though your memory is correct regarding the facts of Ben-Jared's brief tenure with this court," affirmed the general, "let us not begrudge the man for pursuing his true calling. As we speak, do not his merchant ships number more than any others and return to our coastal cities on the Mediterranean from ports abroad with goods of the finest quality? Does not the great trade empire which bears his emblem stretch from the desert of the Negev to the great river Euphrates?

"And let us not forget his renown for training others in the noble arts of selling and influence. The ambitious and bright journey to seek his counsel and return to their regions steeped in the principles which bring prosperity. Countless traders has he mentored to become merchants, merchants to suppliers, and suppliers to leaders of their own caravans. His esteem among the people, as well as the undeniable demonstration of his leadership skills, indicates that he is our best choice for the job. Furthermore," continued the general, "his presence at the helm will influence the caravan leaders - many of whom credit their fortunes to his schooling - to conquer their fears and return to their routes."

And so the matter was brought to a vote. With five of the council members in favor and one abstaining, it was decided that Efram Ben-Jared would be the candidate nominated to lead the treasury during the perilous days ahead. It was also determined that Darius would be the cabinet member entrusted to carry the council's invitation to the great merchant trader's complex in Megiddo.

Aside from the rumors regarding the immensity of the old man's wealth and the occasional passing comment from his father years ago, Darius knew little of the man behind the stories.

Even less did he know, that by nightfall three days hence, a mysterious set of writings would fall into his hands and his courage would be tested like never before if he and its message were to survive.

CHAPTER TWO

—— ⌘ ——

DARIUS AROSE THE NEXT MORNING shortly before dawn. Though the council meeting had lasted well into the wee hours he was determined to get an early start, for the city of Megiddo was some seventy miles to the north of Jerusalem and would require a full day's journey by horse and chariot. The urgency of the matter likewise contributed to his desire to begin at once his task.

The duration of his stay in Megiddo would last for at most two days, depending upon when a meeting could be arranged with Efram Ben-Jared; consequently, the personal belongings he packed were few. In his leather satchel were his garments, the dossier on Ben-Jared and two empty water skins which he would fill at the spring fed well at the city square en route to the stables. Before leaving he checked again to make certain he had packed the royal letter addressed to Ben-Jared which requested a meeting. This would be dispatched to the great merchant trader's complex upon his arrival in the city of Megiddo.

The royal stables were located in the southeast corner of Jerusalem approximately three-fourths of a mile from Darius' quarters on lower Zion Road. With the fast approaching daylight and the commotion of the streets as his allies, Darius' concern regarding Prince Re'boam's spies was greatly reduced; thus, he made his way along the main street of commerce in lieu of travelling the narrow side streets.

As the sun rose over the eastern part of the city Jerusalem was slowly transformed from the sleepiness of the night before into a city which teemed with activity. Darius continued toward the stables and observed that the vendors and merchants had already unshuttered their stalls and shops and were setting out their fresh produce, goods and merchandise in preparation for the day's commerce. *One has to rise very early to beat these enterprising souls.* Darius marveled as he passed through the hive of activity. He had always been an early riser, yet try as he may, was not able to remember a time when he had ever started the day earlier than the traders and merchants on this street. After filling his water skins at the well in the city square Darius walked across the street to a produce vendor's stall and purchased some cheese, dates and raisin cakes for the trip.

Upon his arrival at the royal stables Darius discovered that General Nebo's chief lieutenant had arrived before daybreak and arranged for a stallion and chariot for the journey. Because the directive had come from the general himself, the stable master asked no questions regarding the nature of the trip as Darius loaded his personal belongings, the water skins and a bushel of oats for the horse.

"The general's lieutenant has requisitioned these items for you as well," said the stable master as he handed Darius a large duffel containing a breastplate and sword, a crossbow with arrows and a bronze shield.

"Your chariot carries the seal of the royal guard and thus, offers a fair amount of protection against the robbers and thieves who dwell among the cliffs. But," he continued with a hint of concern in his voice, "one can never be too prepared." Darius gladly accepted the items. It had been several years since his stint in the royal cavalry, yet he felt comfortable knowing he could use his weaponry if the need arose.

After the chariot was loaded and the items secured for travel the chief stable hand led Darius to the stalls and pointed to a glistening black Arabian stallion. "The general's lieutenant has arranged for you one of the finest horses in all the land. He is a spirited beast who answers to the name of Keiron. He runs like the wind and will serve you well." The stable hand haltered the horse and prepared him for the chariot as Darius ran his hand along its sleek mane and marveled at its beauty.

Many years prior, King Solomon had imported nearly three thousand of these beautiful animals from the kingdoms of Egypt and Celicia; now the herd numbered over twelve thousand. Approximately one-third was stabled in Jerusalem, with the remainder spread equally at King Solomon's garrisons throughout the kingdom. These fine horses were a source of pride for all of Israel and the people cheered when the horses and charioteers passed by in formation during the great festivals.

The sun was completely risen now and Darius made a final glance at his maps before embarking. *Barring any unforeseen troubles I should arrive at the gates of Megiddo within ten hours.* He mentally calculated as he led his horse toward the eastern gate of the walled city. Once outside of Jerusalem he would head north on the East Road for approximately two miles as he circled Jerusalem, then west toward the Mediterranean Sea for twenty-five miles. From there he would link with the great inland trade route called Via Maris until connecting with the road to Megiddo. His trip would take him from the hills of Jerusalem through the heavily forested Plain of Sharon and over the Yarkon River. And finally, just prior to reaching Megiddo, he would travel up the mountainous pass that would take him through the southern-most portion of the Carmel range and down into the city on the other side.

Though the trip would take most of the day and would require a consistently brisk pace, he would enjoy the sights of the diverse and beautiful landscape of the interior of the kingdom.

"EASY THERE, KEIRON," Darius said to his horse as he pulled in the reins ever so slightly. The late afternoon sun lingered on the horizon to his left as he crested the southern peaks of Mount Carmel. The horse, like Darius, seemed to sense that they were close to their destination and fought to pick up the gait. Darius brought his horse to a slow walk as they approached a vista on the trail. From his vantage point he could see the city of Megiddo in the valley below. Aside from a stop at a small village for his midday meal and two brief stops along the way to rest and water his horse, he had traveled the entire day. He was dusty, tired and ready to find a suitable inn at which to refresh himself. "Steady on old friend," he said to his horse as they headed down the mile long pass to the city, "we'll have you watered and curried within the hour."

The city of Megiddo had been in existence for centuries but had only recently come under Jerusalem rule; it was now one of the key trade cities of King Solomon's empire. Because of its strategic location near the Via Maris trade route, the king had invested heavily in the fortification and modernization of the city. Its aqueduct system, garrison and massive storehouses were as sophisticated as any in the great kingdoms of the East.

The road leading to the city stirred with activity in the late afternoon. The main gate would close for the evening in less than four hours and the traders and vendors not connected with the larger caravans scurried about in an effort to finish the day's business and retire within the confines of the city. Though Darius knew of Megiddo, this was his first actual visit to the city. He approached the main gate and fell in behind a small trade caravan arriving from the coast.

Once inside the gates Darius headed east on what appeared to be the primary thoroughfare through the city and stopped at a street-side bazaar of spice and produce vendors to inquire about residence for the night. The proprietor of a small vegetable stand had nearly finished closing his cart when Darius pulled up. "Excuse me, sir," Darius called to the man. "Where might a traveler to your fair city find lodging for himself and his animal?"

The man, a jovial Hebrew, took one look at Darius' royal chariot and immediately sized him to be a man of means. "Such a pity," said the man, shaking his head. "My nephew owns a small inn not five hundred paces from here and could certainly use the profits derived from your patronage. But," he lowered his voice and glanced quickly over his shoulder on the unlikely chance that his nephew was listening to the conversation, "his dilapidated building is sorely in need of renovation and I do not think it would be to your liking." He continued to gaze with admiration at Darius' horse and chariot. "No, you would be much more suited to dwell at the inn called Tel Gazor. They have an excellent dining facility and a suitable place to stable your fine animal. Oh, and yes," he continued, "the naturally heated springs of Agmaram are but a stone's throw away. It is a most pleasant place to bathe and refresh after a long journey." Darius graciously thanked him after receiving directions. He smiled to himself as he pulled away and wondered if the enthusiastic man received a commission from the owner of the Tel Gazor Inn.

Darius located the inn and pulled his chariot under the portico at the front entrance where he was immediately met by two young men; one secured the halter of his horse and the other hurried to the back of the chariot and began unloading Darius' belongings. Darius reached into his money purse and gave each a silver coin. He gave an additional coin to the young man in charge of the horse, with instructions to purchase a bundle of carrots to feed the horse after his oats and watering.

He made his way to the front reception area of the inn and, after securing a room, asked the proprietor at the desk, "Are you familiar with the great merchant trader who is known as Efram Ben-Jared?"

The proprietor, who had been intently focused on his ledger, was at first startled by the question but beamed with pride as he responded. "Oh yes, sire; I know him well, for you see, Master Ben-Jared is my partner in this inn. With his capital and my energy this humble concern has prospered now for nearly ten years." He further informed Darius that his inn was just one of many enterprises in the city that Ben-Jared had encouraged and nurtured with similar partnership arrangements.

"Yes, I have heard of his reputation as a builder of wealth and I am glad to hear of your prosperity," said Darius as he reached into his satchel and removed the royal letter addressed to Ben-Jared. "Would you be most kind to have this correspondence delivered to his complex right away?" The proprietor handed the letter to the young clerk seated at his right and whispered the instructions in his ear. The clerk took one look at the royal seal and nearly fell over himself as he agreed to handle the matter personally and immediately. A task such as this for the king's emissary would certainly mean a healthy bonus.

Darius received a latchkey and was directed to the stairs which led to the second floor and his suite of rooms that overlooked the rear courtyard. Upon entering he unpacked his garments, then collected his robe and a towel and returned to the lobby to secure directions to the springs of Agmaram. He had been on the road for nearly eleven hours and was ready for a hot bath, a steam and some relaxation.

Following his return to his room Darius had rested for approximately one hour when he was awakened by a knock at his door. "Yes, who is it?" He rose from his cot and gathered his robe.

"Begging your pardon for the interruption, sire, I have a reply to the correspondence which was sent to Efram Ben-Jared." Darius opened the door and was greeted by the clerk from the front desk.

"Master Ben-Jared's servant awaits your response in the lobby, sire," said the young man as he handed Darius a rolled parchment. Darius removed the bronze ring which secured the scroll and read the note:

My dear sir,

Thank you for your kind letter. It is not often that one receives correspondence from the king's council; accordingly, I would be most honored to meet with you to discuss any matters you deem appropriate. Please accept my invitation to join me this evening for a late supper. If this is acceptable, my servant Jelor will escort you to my compound at your convenience.

Most sincerely,
Efram Ben-Jared

Darius re-rolled the note and rewarded the young man with a gold sovereign. "Instruct Ben-Jared's servant that I gladly accept his master's invitation and will meet him in the lobby within the half-hour."

The clerk returned to the first floor as Darius removed a tunic and cloak from the oak wardrobe, quickly re-read the dossier within his leather satchel and prepared himself to meet this man called Efram Ben-Jared, the great merchant trader of Megiddo.

CHAPTER THREE

—— ⌒⌒ ——

"I AM JELOR AND WILL ESCORT YOU to Master Ben-Jared's complex," said the distinguished Samaritan who greeted Darius as he descended the stairs. "Your horse is no doubt stabled for the night," he continued as they walked through the foyer and into the warm night air, "therefore we shall journey in my master's carriage. And I shall return you to the inn at your leisure."

Under the portico of the inn sat a glistening four-man chariot, its cedar wood frame intricately carved and stained with the deep red dye derived from the edom plant. The interior rails were upholstered with the finest Phoenician leather and its exterior was trimmed in hammered bronze. *Even General Nebo's personal chariot would look out of place next to this fine ride,* thought Darius as he admired the richly appointed carriage.

Jelor adroitly maneuvered the two stallions as they pulled the chariot down the boulevard known as Broad and exited the city via the North gate. From there he turned left on the road which would eventually lead to the port city of Haifa on the Mediterranean. "Master Ben-Jared's complex is approximately two miles northwest of here on a small hill overlooking the plains. We shall be there in no time," he pronounced as he lightly cracked the whip on the stallion on the right.

The lights of Megiddo grew dim as Darius made out what appeared to be a small walled city on the summit of the hill directly ahead of them. "Many years ago this complex was occupied by the son of the governor of Damascus and was used as the south-ern-most outpost for the distribution of the Syrian's trade," offered Jelor. "Following their fall and the subsequent occupation of this region by your people, Master Efram purchased the entire com-pound from King Solomon's district official and has utilized the facilities as the headquarters for his vast trade empire."

They made their way up the hill and stopped at the sentry outpost, some twenty paces from the main gate. Two stoic guards armed with sword were posted at the small stone shack, while four more armed with crossbow patrolled from the top of the 15-foot tall stone wall which surrounded the compound. Jelor nodded to his fellow Samaritans at the post and they motioned for him to pro-ceed toward the gate. Within a moment, unseen men from inside the compound rolled aside the large wooden gates.

"We are somewhat isolated from the garrison of Megiddo," explained Jelor as he noticed Darius' interest in the security measures. "The goods stored here within my master's compound, were they to be stolen by those with evil desires and exchanged for gold, would bring a lifetime of wealth to a thousand men. But," he added with some pride, "this is not likely to happen. My brethren from Samaria are the finest and most loyal guards in the land and it is our honor and duty to protect Master Efram's interests."

As they passed through the gate Darius' attention was immediately drawn to the stunning central garden which served as the focal point of the entire complex. A genuine oasis in the midst of the desert, the garden was enormous, with lush and mature landscaping that was regal in its beauty. Jelor circled the garden for approximately one-eighth of a mile on the road which ringed it and halted the chariot at the main entrance. He tied the horses to one of the many posts placed there for the purpose and indicated for Darius to follow him.

The formal entrance to the garden was delineated by a hand laid stone walkway, wide enough for two chariots, abreast, to pass upon it. The walkway was set between two in-ground rectangular stone ponds, each approximately forty paces in length. Darius admired the stone mason's handiwork as he observed the pools and towering pillars which rose out of the water on either side of him. In the center of the walkway was a row of neatly pruned olive trees which provided ample shade for the entire length of the path. Darius' appreciation for the beauty and design of the garden was apparent to Jelor as they walked along.

At its end, the walkway opened to the upper rear terrace of a small open-air amphitheater. Darius and Jelor stood near the steps at the rim of the half-bowl shaped facility and peered downward. From their point at the top, the land sloped steeply away from them to reveal a stone staging area and lectern at the bottom. Darius counted three terraced ledges which had been cut into the grass hillside, each with a row of limestone benches upon which to sit. Much too small to accommodate the minstrel shows which roamed the countryside, the facility was closer in size to the grand lecture room within the palace at Jerusalem. By Darius' estimation it appeared capable of seating comfortably fifty to sixty people.

Darius had seen drawings of Babylon's great Calidrome arena, at which the multitudes would gather to hear the popular orators of the day, and was struck by the similarity of this miniature version of the facility. He looked at Jelor with genuine curiosity as to why a replica of the great theater would be located here within Efram Ben-Jared's compound.

Jelor sensed his puzzlement and explained. "Though having never sought it, Master Efram has gained much notoriety through the years for his teachings and orations. Surely his renown has reached Jerusalem as well?" Darius nodded. "I shall tell you the story of how it began," continued Jelor.

"Several years ago, after his reputation as a great merchant trader had been firmly established, a handful of his struggling vendors requested that he share with them the knowledge which had caused him to prosper. Honored to have been asked, he willingly obliged their sincere request and began to counsel them in the methods and principles which had led to his prominence.

"As their application of these truths dramatically improved their fortunes, others took notice and likewise sought the counsel of Master Efram. What was birthed as an informal tutoring session for a few young vendors has grown into a thrice-annual assemblage of would-be leaders from far and wide. This amphitheater was built to accommodate the increasing number of attendees."

"Are all of those whom attend employed within the bounds of his trade empire?" inquired Darius.

"No," replied Jelor, "and thus proves the truth of one his teachings. For it seems the more that Master Efram has shared - even with those from whom he will receive no direct benefit from their prosperity - the greater his enterprise and esteem have grown."

The two men remained for a moment longer at the top of the terrace, then retraced their steps through the garden and returned to the horses which awaited them.

Continuing on the road which circled the garden, Jelor directed the chariot down a narrow arterial street which led to a two-story stone building in the southeast section of the compound. Because of its design, the fine detailing of the masonry work and the manicured landscaping surrounding it Darius assumed this structure to be the main residence facility. Its size though, was massive, and comparable to the stately administration building in the royal city. Aside from the king's palace he had seen nothing in his travels even remotely approaching its grandeur.

Jelor halted the chariot on the crushed stone circular drive in front of the mansion and motioned to the entrance. "It has been my pleasure to serve you, sire. If you will kindly proceed to the residence my brother Jabul will greet you." Darius thanked the conscientious driver and proceeded up the stepped stone walkway to the main entrance.

As promised, Darius was immediately met by Jabul, an equally distinguished Samaritan. "Won't you come in, sire. We have been expecting you." He bowed at the waist and extended his right hand toward the foyer. "Master Efram will be detained momentarily, but has asked that I show you to the great room. May I offer you a cool drink to refresh your thirst?"

"Yes, that would be most appreciated," said Darius.

Jabul snapped his fingers twice, and within seconds a servant appeared with a tray of refreshments. With the servant following behind, Jabul led Darius across the polished stone floor of the foyer and down three steps to the atrium-like great room. From the bronze framed paintings to the intricate detail work of the moldings and trim, to the delicate ivory carvings and porcelain vases showcased within the niches of the plastered walls the room was a picture of understated elegance. Darius marveled at the sheer beauty surrounding him.

The oil-fed sconces which adorned the walls and provided a soft, ambient light, appeared to be made of solid gold. The rugs from Persia upon the marble floor and the beautifully upholstered sofas and lounges were of royal quality. To the left of the dressed stone fireplace in a corner along the west wall stood a solitary sixty-string harp in its stand, while five giant palm trees lined the south facing wall and reached for the thirty-foot high ceiling. The room was enormous in size, yet because of the grouping of the tasteful and exquisite furniture could equally accommodate a gathering of one hundred or an intimate evening for two. This was indeed an impressive estate.

Jabul motioned for the servant to set the tray on one of the limestone pedestals, where he poured a goblet of the beverage and offered it to Darius. "This is a favored drink of my people," said Jabul. "Made from the juice of the papaya, banana and orange. It is most refreshing."

Judging by his refined manners, impeccable dress and the deference extended to him by the other servant Darius surmised that Jabul was the man who directed the entire household. "Master Efram should arrive within a few moments. Please be comfortable." He then ascended the three steps which led to the foyer and departed from the room.

Darius enjoyed his beverage as he admired the large oil painting on canvas hung above the fireplace. Having spent a summer of his adolescence in the coastal city of Jaffa he recognized the scene at once. It was of the harbor of the great city at sunset and was painted from the perspective of a ship anchored some five hundred yards off the coast. As his mind recalled memories of days gone by he heard a muffled cough and a distinguished voice behind him.

"I love to visit the sea. It is a most invigorating environment, do you not agree?" said the voice.

Darius turned and saw an elderly man who appeared to be in his early to mid-sixties. He was a man of slightly below average height, and whose skin was tanned and weathered from years in the desert sun. Darius noticed nothing remarkable about the man's physical appearance except two things: his eyes twinkled with life and his smile conveyed warmth and sincerity.

"I am Efram Ben-Jared and it is my pleasure to have you in my home," said the elderly man as he extended his hand to his guest. Though lacking in stature and the chiseled features often associated with charismatic leaders, he radiated confidence yet carried himself with an air of humility. Darius liked him immediately.

After a few moments of polite conversation Jabul entered from the west hall. "Excuse me, sire, dinner will be served in one half an hour."

"Good," said Efram. "This will allow just enough time for me to show our esteemed guest the inner workings of our operation." And with that he led Darius out the main entrance of the mansion and across the crushed stone drive to a covered walkway which led to the vast distribution center.

As they strolled through the various storehouses Darius calculated that at least eighty workers scurried about unloading and sorting the bounty from a train of cargo wagons. "We are not usually working this late into the evening," said Efram. "But this very afternoon a caravan load of goods arrived from our ships at the port of Haifa. The workers you see are preparing the merchandise for distribution on the morrow to our emporiums and caravan leaders throughout the kingdom."

As the tour continued Efram stopped periodically to inspect the new merchandise or to chat with one of the workers. Darius marveled that his host seemed to know each of the dockhands by name. The workers, in turn, responded to their leader with genuine fondness and respect.

Darius silently noted how this contrasted with the environment he had witnessed at the royal storehouses in Jerusalem. No matter how much the supervisors threatened and cajoled and reprimanded, the workers at the royal docks seemed to do only the barest minimum to avoid punishment.

"I notice that your workers appear contented in their labors and go about their tasks without constant prodding from their superiors," said Darius to his host as he relayed the stories of the work environment in Jerusalem. "I cannot believe that the workers of Megiddo are of a different constitution than the workers of my city. To what do you owe the striking difference in spirit?"

The elderly man smiled as he mulled the question. "Over the years, through many failings in my efforts to inspire, I have learned a few important truths. First, people will give their best only when they are encouraged and rewarded for a task well done. If the only reward they receive is the whip upon their back when their labors fall short, they will soon learn to do only that amount of work which will keep the whip from their back, and no more. And second," said Efram as he picked up a bolt of purple fabric from an open bundle, "a leader will secure commitment to his cause *only* when he places the success of his people ahead of his own. Neither riches nor respect will affix to his name lest he labors with the goal that his people prosper first.

"Sadly, I was slow to comprehend this most basic of laws," continued Efram as he returned the bolt of fabric to its bin. "At the outset of my venture into commerce I was driven by a zeal to fill my coffers with gold and I foolishly demanded my workers to labor with this as our common goal. I soon discovered that my selfish dreams did nothing to inspire them, and their work would stop promptly at the end of each shift......or worse, would halt completely if I left the building. Also was it so with the traders I commissioned to market my goods. Though my passion for prosperity pushed me to excel I was not able to infuse this same spirit within their hearts. To my discouragement and dismay my words of persuasion rang empty and my appeals for increased productivity landed upon deaf ears."

"It is difficult to fathom such a scenario," replied Darius, "for the workers I see before me attend to their tasks with an obvious sense of pride. And the traders who market your goods are esteemed as the most prosperous in the land. How were you able to secure such a change?"

Efram hesitated for a moment as he looked out over the work area. "Allow me to answer by giving the illustration of Be'lar, the leader of my caravans from the south." He motioned to the middle aged man counting the bales of linen being loaded onto one of the smaller wagons. "Many years ago Be'lar had a young son who demonstrated much promise in his studies. This was a source of great pride for Be'lar and he desired to give his son all the help his own father had been unable to give him. Unfortunately, as a modestly compensated dockhand, Be'lar was not able to pay for the necessary tutoring which would allow his son to progress.

"He came to me seeking the funds to finance the dream which he harbored, but as my business was still in its early years and the profits were slim I was not able to offer him an increase in wage. Nonetheless, I was moved by his desire and sought to find a way to assist in its fulfillment. As is often the case," said Efram, his eyes suddenly sparkling as he related the fond memory, "*an opportunity arrived when we began to seek it.*

"Then, as now, the large bales of cargo shipped to our warehouse arrived securely bound in rope. Because the bales would be opened and sorted into smaller lots for distribution we had no usage for this rope and simply discarded it as waste. I immediately summoned Be'lar to my office and explained the situation with the wasted rope. I encouraged him to discover a usage for the rope and suggested that he market it to a willing buyer at the price of his choosing. Any profits derived from his endeavor would be shared equally between us. He was quite intrigued by this arrangement and set out that very evening to make it work.

"Within two days," continued Efram, "he stopped by my office with a smile as large as the half moon itself and proceeded to tell me of the reason behind his delight. 'Sire, you will never guess what has happened,' Be'lar said to me as he beamed with satisfaction. 'My cousin, who is in the employ of Cabo the tentmaker, casually mentioned to me that his boss was dissatisfied with the supplier of twine used to bundle the tent stakes and poles he offers for sale. Sensing an opportunity,' he informed me, 'I immediately rushed home and cut several two-foot lengths of our rope as samples to show Master Cabo. He was pleased with the quality of the rope as well as my price and has agreed to purchase all that I can secure for him. Here is your share of the profits from my first sale,' he said as he proudly handed me a few coins of silver.

"He could have handed me a sack of gold and my joy from receiving it would have paled to the satisfaction I received from sharing in his success," said a smiling Efram. "From that moment my thinking was transformed," he then said softly, "for when I focused on my *people* instead of my *profits* my business and stature began to grow.

"Today, fully two-thirds of my income is distributed to the very people who labor to generate it, each according to his level of effort. If, as you say, my people embrace their tasks with great pride it can be for two reasons only: first, they know that they will share abundantly in the gold which is generated by their labors. But second and more importantly," he said with obvious conviction, "I neither push them nor prod them to labor for *me*. If I goad them it is only in the direction of their dream, for when they have prospered, so too shall I."

As they made their way back to the main residence one sentence uttered by the elderly man lingered in Darius' mind. *When I focused on my people instead of my profits my business and stature began to grow....*

In the silence of the brief walk it occurred to Darius that the rumors he'd heard were true: Efram Ben-Jared was indeed a man of significant wisdom.

CHAPTER FOUR

—— ⌒∞⌒ ——

"LET US ENTER THROUGH THE KITCHEN," said Efram with a mischievous grin as he led his guest across the side court-yard. "I like to surprise the cooks." From there he escorted Darius into an enclosed atrium which connected to the culinary wing of the mansion via a set of double doors.

The aroma emanating from the kitchen was a heavenly mixture of turmeric and garlic, with a hint of lemon and butter.

"My chef, Mahedi, is from the land of the Ganges and is a master with the spices of his native country. I trust that his dish-es will be to your liking."

After washing at the basin situated in an alcove off the kitchen Efram and Darius were seated at the large algum wood table in the great dining hall. Darius surveyed the naan bread with dipping sauces, the seasoned rice dishes, the grilled meats and other assorted delicacies laid out before him. The hunger in his stomach reminded him that he had not eaten since his midday meal, some nine hours earlier. Following a brief, yet sincere prayer of thanksgiving by Efram the two men began to partake of the feast in front of them.

Within moments Efram inquired of his friends and acquaintances that remained in the king's service. As best as he could Darius informed his host of the comings and goings of the elder scribes and clerks and attempted to fill in the gap caused by the thirty-year period since Efram's days as a young apprentice in the royal court.

"It seems but yesterday that I was studying under Mabarro, the great teacher of scribes," Efram said wistfully. "My, how my life would have been different had I remained in Jerusalem."

After a moment of quiet reflection Efram then directed the conversation to the matters at hand. "You have journeyed far to visit me and I trust it was not for the purpose of having your ears tickled by the stories and recollections of an old scribe. Tell me, why have you honored me with your visit?"

Darius paused as he folded his linen napkin and placed it in on the table beside his gold cup. "As you are certainly aware, sire," he began, "a leadership crisis of the severest magnitude threatens to destroy our nation. Our King Solomon lay upon his deathbed and the entire kingdom teeters at the precipice of danger. The actions taken in the days to come could well have repercussions for generations to follow."

For the next quarter hour Darius explained in great detail the fear and trepidation surrounding the king's heir, the danger of revolution by the northern tribes, and finally, the debilitating illness of Baruch, head of the treasury.

"And so," Darius concluded, "it is the latter problem which has necessitated my visit to you this evening. The situation at the treasury is extreme and requires immediate attention. Because of your expertise in the areas of finance and commerce the royal council has determined that you are the best-qualified candidate to lead it through this difficult time. We hope that you will give the matter serious consideration."

"Who am I that such an invitation should be extended?" Efram replied after a moment of silence. "I am but a humble man of trade who has risen to prominence only by the blessing of the Almighty." He clearly was overwhelmed by the invitation. "I am completely unworthy of such a position, but if the king's council has faith in me, then I would be most honored and willing to give my all in service to our nation."

Darius and the other council members had anticipated an affirmative response and had prepared an abundance of financial reports for Efram to pore over before his arrival at the treasury.

"We had hoped that you might arrive at your new post in Jerusalem within the fortnight. Will this be possible?" asked Darius as he handed the materials to his elderly host.

Efram accepted the leather bound collection of reports and smiled. "That will be ample time to prepare my affairs. I learned long ago the importance of picking capable leaders, empowering them to make decisions... and then staying out of their way." He chuckled as he continued, "In fact, my enterprise seems to do better when I am *not* interfering in the day to day operations."

As the meal came to a close and the servants gathered the plates and bowls, Darius, cognizant of the lateness of the hour, said to his host, "You have been most kind to allow me to dine at your table, Efram Ben-Jared. I am honored to have been invited into your home." He smiled warmly to his host as they rose from the table and grasped hands. Though the days ahead promised peril and uncertainty Darius looked forward to working closely with his new friend and elder mentor. "Our time together has been most pleasant," he continued, "but regrettably, it is late and I have stayed much longer than I had planned." He gathered his cloak and satchel and prepared for the return to his room at the inn.

"The lateness of the hour is of no concern to me," replied Efram. "But sadly it is also the hour when the robbers, like the possum, crawl from behind their rocks to roam the roads. With your permission I will send my capable servants Jelor and Jabul to the inn to gather your belongings so that you might dwell here for the evening, within the safety of my compound. Besides, our conversation has stirred my memories and has kindled within me the desire to share them. My servants have suffered the ramblings of this old man a hundred times, no doubt, so I would be most honored if you would agree to stay."

Disappointed not in the least and touched by his host's sincere hospitality, Darius accepted the offer and they adjourned to the landscaped inner courtyard. The elderly man clapped his hands and within moments Mahedi the chef arrived with a plate of sweet cakes and a pot of tea. "I know that too much of the baker's confections render my garments too small," chuckled Efram, "but at my age - who cares?"

Turning to his servant he instructed him to send Jelor and Jabul to the inn to gather Darius' belongings and to have them placed in the guest suite of the east wing of the compound. "Oh, and most importantly," he winked toward Darius as he called out to the departing servant, "no matter how loudly I clap, *do not bring another plate of these sweets!*"

For nearly half an hour the two men sat silently in the leather-strapped chairs by the stone fountain and enjoyed their tea and cakes in the pleasant ambience of the summer night. A gentle breeze stirred the air as the water from the fountain provided a soothing underscore to the setting.

After finishing their cakes Darius was the first to speak. "You are from a long line of distinguished scribes, Efram. Tell me, how is it that you left the profession of your fathers and became a leader of such great influence in the arena of trade?"

A slight smile crossed the elderly man's face as he pondered the question; for a moment he did nothing but reflect. With a faraway longing in his voice he then began to reminisce.

"I was but a young man, employed by my father in King Solomon's court," he said softly. "And I was easily and foolishly impressed by the trappings of wealth and status which surrounded me.

"I observed the most prosperous leaders of our land and how the people catered to their every whim and want. I perceived their wealth and influence as power and decided that I, too would rise to such heights for the spoils it would bring." He paused, as if the naivete of his youth embarrassed him still.

"Thanks be to God, my father recognized the misdirection of my desire and gently guided me to the proper course. *To grow in stature as well as in purse,* he admonished me, *you must never seek to exalt yourself. Rather, seek only to serve. For it is only in your service to others will you be elevated to a position of influence and honor and wealth.*"

A comforting presence settled in among them as the wind rustled the palm fronds overhead. Darius found himself captivated by the softly spoken, yet powerful words of the elderly man and memories from his youth filled his mind. For the blink of an eye he was twelve and sitting at his own father's knee. *Oh, what I would give to re-live just one of those moments,* thought Darius as he listened to the great man before him recount the journey of his life....

CHAPTER FIVE

—— ✑ ——

Efram Ben-Jared

THE WHOLE OF JERUSALEM was abuzz with the charisma of the new young monarch. King Solomon was but a young man of twenty-three and had been on the throne barely one thousand days, yet already the people of his kingdom sensed the promise of greatness which radiated from him. Although Solomon's father, the great warrior king David, had secured the borders of Israel and brought the twelve factious tribes together as one, it was widely perceived that Solomon would be the sovereign who would transform the fledgling nation into a bona-fide empire of prominence and wealth.

Among the new young king's many talents was his proficiency as an architect. His grand designs for the soon to be constructed Temple had energized the people and given them a sense of unity not seen since the days of Moses and the exodus from Egypt. The future for the young nation of Israel was promising and the people discerned it.

Efram Ben-Jared placed his quill in the holder on his desk and rubbed his eyes as he stood for a moment to stretch. It was nearly four in the afternoon and he had just completed transcribing the eleventh of twelve copies of a relatively minor royal edict which would be delivered to the provincial governors. *With any luck I will have this assignment finished in two hours; then I will speak with father,* he promised himself as he removed a fresh piece of papyrus and began the laborious process of transcribing letter for letter the twelfth and final copy from the original.

Efram was an ambitious young man with a mind as keen for strategies as for letters and figures and his superiors routinely commented on his skills. And yet, though he pushed himself to excel in his work, something was lacking. The challenge of being a scribe was fading and his instincts told him that his real talents remained hidden and untested.

From the small window above his desk on the second floor of the king's administration building Efram observed the hum of construction activity occurring throughout Jerusalem. For the past two and one-half years he had monitored with great interest the expansion of the city, as well as the massive excavation underway in preparation for the building of the great Temple.

Like all of Jerusalem Efram shared a sense of pride at the prosperity in progress, yet a feeling of personal dissatisfaction increasingly dominated his thoughts. *Builders and traders less than my age are becoming richer by the day while I toil on trivialities in this closet of an office*. He struggled to focus his mind on the work at hand as he daydreamed of wealth and notoriety for himself. *Soon, I, too will join their ranks*.

Efram's father, Jared of the tribe of Levi, had been a key scribe in King David's court and had played an important role in the transition from King David's administration to the new King Solomon. Now, as the royal secretary of King Solomon's court, he was a man of prominence in Jerusalem and like any father in a similar situation sought to secure a position of status for his son. *Father has sacrificed greatly for me to be here. He will not take this news well,* Efram thought to himself, still unsure how he would explain the decision which was certain to disappoint the one man that he admired most.

Efram Ben-Jared was the eldest son of Jared and his wife Hannah, and from the time of his birth it was expected that he would become a scribe like his father, and his father before him. His people had always placed great significance on the value of the written word and his family lineage boasted of a continuous succession of scribes dating to the time of Moses, when the only means of recording was to inscribe the letters on wet clay tablets. For an eldest son like Efram it was unthinkable to pursue any profession other than the one of his ancestors.

Further complicating the matter was the fact that Efram shared the same month of birth with his new king and had, due to his father's prominence in King David's court, spent his early years as a child playmate of the young Solomon. For the duration of his young life Efram Ben-Jared had been groomed for a position in the royal court, yet now was on the verge of discarding it all to follow a different course. He did not expect his father, or any one else for that matter, to understand his decision, but the plans for his life did not include a career as a royal scribe.

Efram applied the finishing touches to the twelfth and final copy of the royal correspondence and waved it in the air before placing it on the wooden rack on his desk to dry. As he straightened his work area and gathered his thoughts in preparation for the meeting with his father, a sudden surge of intimidation engulfed him as the reality of the moment sank in. The decision he had made with certainty not twenty-four hours earlier now seemed questionable.

He timidly climbed the half flight of stairs which led to the executive floor. As he made his way down the long corridor and approached the reception area of his father's office he noticed that a solitary figure labored on an unseen document in the soft glow of the candlelight. He immediately recognized the elderly man and smiled as he approached the desk.

"Good evening, Obed," said Efram to his father's loyal chief assistant. "Once again the day has slipped away and you remain at your post. Do you never tire of your labors?" Efram playfully chided his father's elderly aide.

"Ah, but a man's work is labor only if he does not enjoy it," said Obed. "I was most fortunate as a young man to stumble upon a profession that brings me a sense of accomplishment and happiness. A man's life will most certainly be blessed if he spends his days in a vocation that he loves. I have, and I count it as success."

They chatted for a moment and then Obed passed along the message from Efram's father. "Master Jared is in consultation with the king, but should arrive at any moment. He has asked that you forgive his tardiness and kindly wait for his arrival." Obed escorted Efram to his father's outer office. The elderly assistant then closed the mahogany double doors and returned to his desk in the reception area.

Efram paced nervously as he waited in the richly decorated room and considered dropping the matter entirely. Any guest to this suite of offices would observe at once that his father Jared was a man of great influence in King Solomon's court and thus, all of the kingdom. Standing in this room Efram was reminded - due to his pedigree, education and training - that he himself might someday occupy this very office were he to continue the journey of the scribe.

Have you gone mad, bellowed the practical voice of reason in his head. *This will someday be yours. And now you wish to throw it away to chase some foolhardy venture?* Efram struggled to control the fear and doubt which rendered him nearly immobile. *No, I must not allow myself to be tempted by the security and status which would accompany a position in the court,* he told himself. *This is not my calling.*

While the conflicting thoughts of reason and desire continued their battle in his mind he turned to his left as he heard the unlatching and opening of a door.

"Greetings, my son," the distinguished elder scribe known as Jared said warmly as he entered from the side door which connected to the king's private offices. "Please forgive my tardiness. Our king required my counsel earlier this afternoon and the matter consumed more time than anticipated. Let us retire to my office where we might discuss what is on your mind."

Efram and his father clasped hands and warmly embraced in the customary greeting. Though at times challenged by the typical father-son battle of wills, their bond was strong and Efram was thankful that mutual affection and respect passed between them. They entered his father's office and were seated at the upholstered chairs by the large window which framed a magnificent view of the city below.

After several moments of awkward and insignificant conversation Jared raised his hand and halted their chat. "My son, I can sense that you are troubled. Tell me, what is the source of your turmoil?"

Efram lifted his gaze from the floor and took a deep breath. "Father, surely you see that our city is prospering all around us. Great fortunes are being created virtually every day and I feel as though the opportunities of this life are passing me by." He stammered to get the words out. "I...I want to participate in the prosperity and become a man of influence."

Jared the elder listened with curious interest as his son paused to calm himself. "I am sorry, father," said Efram, "but I am not content to transcribe the events of others. My heart's desire is to be one of those who influences the event, not one who merely records it after the fact." He had practiced this speech many times over the past day, yet was disappointed at the little amount of conviction his words conveyed as they departed from his mouth.

Jared sat quietly for several moments as he absorbed the disconcerting words. Finally, he responded. "I find your words puzzling, my son. From the days of your primary schooling you have shown great aptitude for the ways of the scribe. Because of this, I, at great cost, have secured your tutelage under the master scribe Mabarro. You are a bright young man with a promising future in this court. And yet, you say that you do not wish to follow in the profession that I, and my father before me, have found so rewarding?"

"Yes...that....is correct," Efram replied meekly. The doubt regarding his decision was suddenly magnified by the carefully reasoned words of his father.

"How is it that I have failed you that you wish to depart from the path which has been prepared for you?"

"Oh, father you have not failed me," Efram replied immediately, somewhat taken aback. He had anticipated disappointment, but not the level of hurt which radiated in his father's voice. "You have given me great opportunity and have imparted significant wisdom into my life. Were I the wealthiest man in the world I would never be able to repay all that you have done for me. But," he continued somberly, "I do not share your enthusiasm for the profession of the scribe. My interests lie elsewhere."

"And what is the path you desire to follow, my son?"

Young Efram hesitated and then said quietly, "I wish to become a leader in commerce and trade and accumulate great wealth." He feared that his answer would greatly disappoint his father, a man who had pursued public service over material riches.

For a moment his father said nothing as he pondered the response of his son. "And why do you wish to accumulate riches?" he said finally.

Efram's face brightened as he explained. "I see how those with gold, title and position are given prominence in our society. I watch the leaders of our people in the market and I note how the masses bow to them and treat them with respect." His enthusiasm was tempered with a touch of youthful anxiety as he continued. "Father, I am most thankful for my position as a scribe, but I fear that if I continue my present path I will toil the length of my days in obscurity. It will never allow me the platform nor the opportunity to be a man of influence and importance among our people."

Jared rose from his seat and walked to the large window to his left. For several moments he did nothing but peer at the city below. Deep in thought, he returned to his seat before speaking. "My son, genuine influence, respect and admiration come from one's character and should never be predicated upon one's gold or title or position. For if the whole of a man's influence is based upon these temporal things, what would happen to him if they were taken away?" Efram looked at his father quizzically, unsure of where the question was leading.

"Allow me to explain," Jared continued. "Do you remember Ibrahim, the late constable of our city? Did he not have a position of influence, as well as gold in his purse?"

"Yes, father," Efram acknowledged.

"And the people did indeed bow to him in the city square

when he passed by, did they not?" Again, Efram nodded his head in agreement. "But I ask you," his father continued, "what happened to his respect following his removal from the office which he held?"

His father proceeded before Efram was able to comment. "I shall tell you. His so-called respect evaporated like a droplet of water on the desert sand. His subordinates deserted him and he eventually died a lonely and bitter man. Do you know why? Because he abused the authority and influence which accompanied his office. The people did not respect nor admire him; they bowed to him only in fear and intimidation. When the end of his days came upon him and his identity was separated from his position, the people no longer had reason to bow to him."

Jared continued with his explanation. "Consider also the example of Delmazzon, the master engineer and builder of walls in our city. He was a man of immense wealth and was given a seat of prominence at assembly because of his lavish and public offerings. But how did his workers and those with whom he dealt in business consider him? Certainly they offered him a measure of respect, but they did so grudgingly and only because his gold was the source of their livelihood. In truth, he was a selfish and egotistical man with no regard for his people. Were it not for his gold he would have had few friends and even less loyalty from his subordinates."

Efram cleared his throat as if to comment, but astutely decided against it as his father proceeded. "No, my son, genuine influence and respect are not related to the size of one's purse or the title upon their door; rather, they come from within," said Jared as he lightly tapped his index finger over his heart. "As proof of this, I ask you to reflect on the story of Alzabar."

Efram smiled at the mention of the late teacher who had

instructed him during the last few years of his adolescence. His esteemed teacher had now been gone for nearly five years, but the mere mention of his name brought back many fond memories.

"Your teacher Alzabar had little in the way of gold, rarely spoke at assembly or in the public forum, and was never bestowed with an official title," said Jared. "And yet the people of our city revered his ways and spoke highly of him. Can you tell me why?"

Once again Jared did not wait for a response. "The answer is simple, my son. *He sought to build others and never himself.* His first concern was for those whom he led and he routinely gave of his time and funds to help the needy of our city. Because of his quiet example others were inspired to join the causes for which he labored, and today, the orphanage which stands on Lower Fountain Street is a lasting tribute to his influence.

"He did not seek the praises of men nor desire accolades and yet there were few among us who were more regarded or highly esteemed. He walked humbly and his words were few, but they carried abundant weight.

"My son, take heed and observe how the lesson of your late teacher's life contrasts with the hordes of would-be leaders who spend their days convincing others of their importance, and who struggle and labor to exalt themselves and their causes. At the end of the day they have nothing to show for their efforts except a reputation for self-promotion. They are so focused on self that they are unable to see the needs and concerns of the very people they profess to help.

"This is an interesting phenomenon, is it not?" said Jared as he leaned forward in his chair. "*If you seek honor and respect you will not find it, for a leader is powerless to elevate himself. It is only when you serve others without regard for self, will honor, respect and lasting success be found."*

As his son listened intently Jared leaned back in his chair and paused, pleased that his words had apparently begun to sink in.

"My son," he then continued, "I am not able to impede your choices, nor would I wish to. Though I am disappointed that you do not find the life of the scribe to your liking, I do not begrudge your desire to succeed as a merchant trader. On the contrary, I applaud your ambition and would that you become the greatest of them all." He then concluded his impromptu lesson with a final illustration.

"It is fine for a man to have a position of influence and the trappings of wealth," he said as he gestured toward the lavish decorations within his impressive office - and then waived them off as if insignificant. "But these are not to be sought as the primary goal. *They should merely be the by-products of the level of service we render.* Thus, as you go forth from this day, I ask only that your desire to rise as a leader be motivated by your desire to serve."

Efram sat in respectful silence assimilating all that he had heard. From the days of his youth he had marveled that his father's words had always spoken wisdom and truth. After a moment of quiet contemplation he bid his father goodnight, exited the administration building via the south doors and made his way to his quarters.

The theme of his father's teaching continued to ring in his ears as he walked the cobblestone streets in the golden twilight of dusk. *Only when I serve others without regard for myself will honor, respect and lasting success be found....*

CHAPTER SIX

— ❧ —

EFRAM STOOD IN THE CENTER OF THE SMALL WARE-
HOUSE he had leased and surveyed the bales, crates and bundles
of unsold merchandise which lined the walls. Discouraged, he
made his way to the rear doors, fastened them and prepared to
retire to his home for the evening. Another day had come and gone
and his till registered but a few copper coins for the effort.

Nearly nine months had passed since he'd left his position
at the royal court and he had little to show for the labor of his days.
What prompted me to undertake such a foolish venture? he
thought in disgust. *I am trained in the humble ways of the scribe,
not in the confident manner of the trader. Of leadership or persuasion I know nothing. Who am I to inspire anyone to labor by
my side?* The questions haunted him as he replayed in his mind
the events that had brought him to this point.

The other young scribes and clerks at court were incredu-
lous at his decision to leave. If anyone of the group had been a
surefire bet to catapult to the king's inner circle, it was Efram. His
father's prominence, his first-rate education and his proficiency
with the quill indicated that he was indeed bound for a career of
substance. But now, by his own choice, it was gone - along with
much of his life savings, most of his hope and all of his confidence.

In his exuberance to begin his journey to wealth and
acclaim Efram had failed to take the appropriate amount of time to

review the entire lot of goods he had committed to purchase. Only too late did he discover the rugs that were threadbare, the sandals that had not a matching twin, the garments and tapestries that had been eaten through by the weevil and the pottery that was cracked or broken. These were the items upon which he had planned to build the foundation of his great wealth, but in truth, would be lucky to return a tenth of his capital outlay.

Likewise had he overestimated his ability to retain the vendors who made up the selling force of his trade route. With the ink not yet dry on his agreement with the previous owner, the eight seasoned traders on whom he had counted to market his goods marched into his office and demanded the lion's share of all future profits. When Efram explained the impossibility of such a demand the group banded together to form a competitive concern and one by one proceeded to pilfer the customers whose patronage was to provide his income.

In the immediate weeks following the departure of the traders Efram had tried without success to commission others in their place. Be they young, old, ambitious or otherwise, he had welcomed many prospective vendors into his fold, but most quick-ly departed upon discovering his less-than-inspiring competence in matters of business. In truth, he could hardly blame them, *for not even rats remain on a sinking ship* he had concluded when the last of the new traders left for more prosperous environs.

His most humiliating defeat cost him dearly in pride and product and came at the hands of a passer-by filled with promises and optimistic projections en route to the coast. Against his better judgement yet desperate to record an entry of sales into his empty ledger, Efram had agreed to consign a wagonload of his best goods to the passing vendor. The deadline for payment was now three moons past and he knew in his heart that neither the vendor nor his merchandise would ever been seen again.

Deceived, deserted and nearing financial ruin he pondered his dilemma and deeply regretted his plunge into commerce.

In an effort to busy himself Efram had sorted and inventoried the goods within his warehouse numerous times over the past several months, each time arriving at the same sad conclusion. While the small inventory of spices were of value, most of the goods were either used or obsolete and but one in three items had any marketable worth.

As the value of his investment dwindled by the day and with few customers to occupy his time, Efram had ample time to reflect on his decision. The grand plans and visions for his life which had inspired him to leave the security he had known were now replaced by misgivings and second-guessing. *In my rush to acquire riches I have committed an act of pure folly,* he dejectedly thought. *How could I have been so foolish?*

Efram struggled to banish the demons of doubt, but to no avail. *Maybe my friends were right. What do you know of business? Of selling? Of motivating and influencing others? You'll be back,* they had exclaimed. The remarks of his peers seemed cutting and belittling at the time; now he had begun to think they were also true.

After securing the building he made his way toward his dwelling and considered his options, but was forced to admit they were few. He had invested nearly all of his available funds in the purchase of the goods on the assumption that the future sales would cover his expenses, overhead and a profit. But this had not occurred and his pool of remaining capital had all but dried up. Failure was inevitable and close by, and he knew it.

Efram searched his mind for any idea which would allow him to salvage his investment. *Maybe I could speak with the traders who had arranged the sale between the previous owner and me? It's possible they might be interested in buying the goods.* As he walked along, this particular idea seemed to gain merit and he picked up his pace. When he arrived at the street which would have taken him to his dwelling he turned right instead and doubled back toward the traders district on the hopes of speaking with the two brothers who had arranged the sale.

THE BROTHERS LOOKED AT EFRAM, then at each other, back again at Efram and finally burst into laughter. The loud and boisterous kind that said *Surely you jest*. Efram stood in silence as they continued their amusement at the explanation of his dilemma and subsequent question. After a moment, the laughter subsided enough for the elder brother to speak. "Kindly explain to us again your unusual request," he said as he winked toward his still laughing brother. The chuckle in his voice indicated that he wished to hear the humorous story all over again.

Efram suddenly felt foolish. "I....I don't seem to be doing too well in my business and had hoped that you might consider purchasing my inventory." He blurted out the words with equal parts anger and shame.

Once again the brothers looked at each other and grinned. The younger one finally replied, his demeanor turned suddenly serious. "We are traders, certainly, but the goods that we sell are of the highest quality. If my memory serves, your goods came from

Zadar the Jebusite, is that correct?"

Efram nodded. "Yes, I believe that was the owner's name."

"Ah, that is most unfortunate," said the younger brother as he shook his head. "Poor Zadar spent years developing and nurturing his reputation as a seller of sub-par goods. No, we would not be able to market your items, for it would be far too damaging to our good name if we were to begin selling inferior merchandise."

You were most willing to arrange the sale to me without concern for your reputation - and gladly received a healthy commission, too, thought Efram as his anger grew.

"But do not despair," said the older brother almost immediately, "there is one possible solution. Might I suggest that you place a notice of sale bulletin at the post at the bazaar in the city square and offer your goods for sale. There is never a lack of young and idealistic would-be caravan leaders seeking an entry into the world of commerce."

"Only set your price high, so that you might bargain, if needed," offered the younger brother as he gently grasped Efram by the arm and led him to the front entrance. "And good luck," he yelled just prior to closing the door behind Efram.

Efram stood on the outer stone pathway for a moment before heading toward the street. He could hear the laughter emanating from inside the building, yet tried to block it out. *Maybe they're right,* he thought. *It's very possible someone could be enticed to purchase the whole lot. After all, I was,* he painfully realized.

He thought more of the idea and reasoned that it just might work. Though much of the pottery inventory was of little value, what of the rugs and linens and other dry goods that had not been eaten through by the weevil? True, they were a season or two out of date, but could they not be salvaged and marketed by someone of greater skill? *Perhaps I could sell the whole lot to a sharp trader who might rebundle the items and offer them for sale in a less sophisticated village or town? If I dust off the cargo and hide the defective items, surely someone might be lured to buy the lot. At least then I might recover a portion of my investment.* Invigorated by this idea Efram headed toward his warehouse.

Upon arriving he went straight to his desk and hurriedly wrote out a notice of sale bulletin. He then walked the three blocks to the bazaar area of the city square and located an information post, where he tacked up his notice of sale. His hope quickly turned to discouragement though, when he realized that the post contained several other such notices and offerings. He then trudged off to his residence, even more disheartened than when he had set out earlier that evening.

THE NEXT MORNING EFRAM ARRIVED AT HIS WARE-HOUSE and was surprised to find a young man waiting at the door.

"Good morning, sire," the young man said cheerfully. "I am Levar and am inquiring of the spices, pottery, dry goods and other merchandise for sale."

"Yes, yes, of course," said Efram. "Do come in." Though he had not anticipated such a quick (or any) response, he was thankful that most of the damaged and worn merchandise had been hidden under the bales and out of sight the day before. As Efram unlocked the door he quickly surveyed the prospective buyer before him and observed that he appeared to be a young

Hebrew man within a year of two of his own age.

"I see from your notice posted at the square that you are asking three measures of gold for the entire lot. May I see the goods in question?" asked the young man enthusiastically.

"That is correct, and yes, you may look around at your leisure," replied Efram as he pointed him to the rear of the warehouse. Though the young man seemed quite interested, Efram viewed the tattered condition of his cloak and the worn appearance of his sandals, and was not overly optimistic regarding the young man's possession of gold for the purchase price.

After several minutes of reviewing the inventory in the warehouse the young man returned to the small office area. "I have recently purchased a cargo wagon," he said, "and am quite anxious to begin my career as a seller of goods in our city. The price that you are asking seems reasonable." He paused as he reached into the small money purse hidden under the belt to his cloak. "Would you accept one gold sovereign as a deposit, with the balance due on the morrow when we finalize the transaction?"

Efram was startled by this interesting turn of events. The young man had not even attempted to bargain over the price. Efram found it hard to believe, but this young man actually seemed to be more naïve in these matters than he had been. *Not my concern,* he quickly thought, *at least I'll get my investment back.*

"That would be most acceptable," replied Efram to the young man's offer as he tried to stifle his eagerness. He removed a piece of papyrus from his desk and hastily wrote out a purchase agreement.

"Good," said the young man with obvious enthusiasm. "Then I shall return on the morrow and we will settle the matter."

He signed his name and the address of his dwelling at the bottom of the page and returned it to Efram, along with the gold sovereign. He shook hands with Efram in farewell, and with that, exited the warehouse and was on his way.

Efram could not believe his good fortune. Barely twelve hours ago he had held out little hope of recovering any of his initial investment. Now, it appeared he would recover most of it. He placed the purchase agreement in his desk drawer and went into the back to straighten up the goods in preparation for tomorrow.

After working most of the day organizing and sorting through the warehouse full of the worn and outdated merchandise, Efram's euphoria over selling the entire lot to the unsuspecting purchaser gradually evolved into guilt. *Honor...serve others without regard for self...integrity...*Strangely, the words of his father haunted him as he labored.

But the buyer had an opportunity to review the merchandise before he bought it, didn't he? Efram sought to assure himself. *Besides, this is the way business is done, is it not? No one pointed out the defective items before I purchased them, why then should I?* The rationalizations played over and over in his mind as he worked.

As the late afternoon approached, Efram determined that a rest was needed from the conflict which raged in his mind. He tucked the purchase agreement in the inside pocket of his cloak for safekeeping, quickly locked the building and set out for the inn called Haja on Lower Fountain Street. *Their chef makes the best lamb stew in the city. A good meal will satisfy the hunger within my stomach and settle the battle within my mind.* He forced himself to think of less stressful matters.

Two blocks from his warehouse he crossed the small wooden bridge over the city aqueduct and headed east on Lower Fountain Street toward the inn, but abruptly stopped when he heard the laughter of children at play. Lost in his thoughts, he had not realized exactly where he was until he heard the children. The battle in his mind ceased and it occurred to him at once what he must do.

EFRAM DESCENDED THE STEPS at the front entrance of the orphanage and headed toward the street. Buntanin, the religious man who had become house director of the orphanage upon Alzabar's death, had thanked him profusely even as Efram explained that much of the goods were of questionable value. But he would hear nothing of Efram's protestations. "We are a thrifty and industrious bunch here at the orphanage and can find ample usage for most anything that is donated," Buntanin had said with obvious gratitude.

Now, just one other matter to remedy, Efram resolved as he rushed down the street.

The small whitewashed dwelling was located in a part of Jerusalem with which Efram was not familiar. He entered the small courtyard through the waist high outer gate and proceeded up the narrow stone path to the entrance. He rapped gently on the door and was greeted by an elderly woman carrying an infant.

"May I kindly speak with Levar?" asked Efram of the woman. She nodded and retreated back into the house. Seconds later Levar appeared at the door and greeted his visitor with a cheerful smile; nonetheless, he was clearly puzzled by the appearance of Efram at his home.

"I've had a change of heart regarding our transaction," Efram said nearly immediately.

Levar was momentarily stunned. "If you've received a better offer, I...I could possibly increase my offer a small amount," he said nervously.

"No, no, that's not it at all," Efram replied meekly. He then explained the entire situation to the young man.

"You are most honorable, kind sir," Levar replied when Efram had finished, "and I am deeply touched by your truthfulness."

Efram said nothing in response as he reached into his money purse, retrieved the single gold sovereign paid as deposit and placed it in the young man's hand. He then turned and walked toward the street which would lead him to his home.

As the evening sun dropped to the horizon behind him Efram trudged toward his residence, resigned to accept his failure. Though he felt a slight sense of honor in that he had not unloaded the goods on the unsuspecting buyer, and was relieved that the orphanage would be able to use at least some of the items, he was forced to admit that he had failed in his quest to become a successful merchant trader.

Upon arriving he entered his room, locked the door behind him and collapsed upon his bed as a profound sense of defeat overwhelmed him. *What will they say when I return to my father, begging for work?* He could imagine the laughter of the other young clerks and scribes which would soon be ringing in his ears. It was a dream now, but tomorrow it would be real and he would have to face it. Exhausted, more of the mind than of the body, he drifted off to sleep.

CHAPTER SEVEN

— ∞ —

EFRAM AROSE THE NEXT MORNING with a sense of dread unknown until now. The failure of his enterprise he'd seen coming the past few months and had prepared his mind, but he had not allowed himself to think of the return to his father in disgrace. Now, the moment he had refused to even consider was upon him. *The pain of my failure as a trader is bearable,* he said to himself, *but the fact that I have failed my father is not.* Demoralized and defeated, he bathed, dressed and departed his dwelling for his father's office to seek forgiveness and an opportunity to return to his work.

His first thought upon arrival at the royal administration building was to sneak in through the less traversed north entrance. This would take him through the rear of the complex, past the custodial areas and eventually up the service stairwell where his chances of seeing anyone he knew were greatly diminished. Unfortunately though, the north entrance was temporarily cordoned off so that the stone masons might repair a segment of the riser of the first floor stairs. To his disappointment Efram was forced to enter through the main south entrance, which would take him directly past the work area of the clerks and scribes he had left but nine months before.

After entering the main floor and proceeding up the grand staircase to the second floor Efram walked along the corridor which opened to the rows of desks occupied by his former peers. Though most acknowledged him with a smile and a quick wave or gesture he felt as though the glares of a hundred eyes seared into his back as he passed by. *Surely they know what a failure I am,* he thought as he made his way to the stairwell which would take him up to the executive level and his father's office.

At the reception area of his father's office Efram was surprised to see that Obed, his father's assistant, was not at his post. He then walked past Obed's empty desk and into the outer room of his father's office. From there he could see that his father's door was open, so he timidly approached it and peeked in.

Jared was at work at his desk, but looked up when he saw his son standing at the door. "Come in my son," he said calmly, "there is something I would like to discuss with you."

Efram walked into the grand office, which was the very symbol of success, and felt even worse than he had earlier in the morning. His father stood and motioned for Efram to have a seat in one of the two chairs which faced his desk.

"My son, I have heard of your kind gesture of yesterday," Jared said immediately after Efram was seated.

Efram was astounded and somewhat embarrassed that his father knew of his visit to the orphanage. He had not planned to speak of the donation to anyone. Besides, he had eventually decided, the goods had so little marketable value that donating them to someone in need was the only honorable thing he could do.

"I do not know of your future plans my son, but in the interim as you consider your options I have a unique task that may be of interest to you." Jared returned to his chair behind the desk and continued with his proposal. "I would not force you to ask, and furthermore, it would be very unwise for us both if I returned you to your previous position. I would be condemned by the other scribes and apprentices in my charge for showing favoritism to my son, and your spirit would eventually wither because your heart is not in the work. Therefore, I think it best if we consider an alternative assignment.....if you would care to hear of this opportunity?"

"Of course, father," Efram said quietly. His confidence had been deeply wounded and he would have gladly taken any position his father offered. And, in a way, he was relieved that his father already knew of his failure and that he would not have to recount it in words that would be humbling and humiliating.

Jared then proceeded. "First, my son, you must forget the pain of your failure and remember only the lesson which it taught you. For the only shame in defeat is to neglect to learn from it." Efram nodded quietly as he listened to his father.

"And second, do not ever be ashamed of attempting a worthy endeavor and failing. A leader achieves greatness, not because he has never tasted the bitter pill of failure, *but because he does not allow his failure to stop him.*

"Now, like the prophets of old, let us look only to the future." The father paused as he removed a piece of papyrus from the bottom drawer of his desk and began to write, the text of which Efram was unclear.

A moment later Jared continued speaking. "As all of our nation knows, our King Solomon is destined for greatness. He humbly walks in the ways of wisdom and prosperity follows his every step. His burgeoning trade empire now expands to the land of the Phoenicians, and points beyond. His royal fleet of trade ships currently under construction will soon sail the seas in search of great and valuable items of trade to return to our land. And above the ground which has been broken on Mount Moriah will someday rise the magnificent Temple, which shall stand for generations as a monument to his adherence to the ways of the Almighty.

"A leader such as ours comes along but once in a thousand years, my son. Thus, it is important that we record the events of his life as a lesson for all that will follow. Herein is the assignment for you to consider." He walked from behind his desk and seated himself in the chair next to Efram.

"I would like you to travel at the side of our King Solomon, learn his ways, observe his methods and preserve the lessons of his life in written form so that future generations of leaders might benefit." Jared paused momentarily, as if to allow the full weight of his proposition to settle. "Is this something that might be of interest to you, my son?"

"I am indebted to you father and will undertake this, or any other task that you ask of me, with gladness," Efram replied. Though the memory of his failure lingered within his spirit, something about this new opportunity piqued his interest and a faint spark of enthusiasm resurfaced in his voice.

"Very well," said Jared as he folded the papyrus upon which he had been writing and handed it to his son. "On the morrow, take this directive to the king's private secretary and await further instructions for beginning this assignment."

"I will not fail you father. I will give this my all and you will be proud of me," the young Efram eagerly replied as he accepted the work order and grasped his father's hand in his.

The wise father smiled and said nothing. He knew that if his son's desire to become a leader in trade was genuine, this assignment with the king would fill him with knowledge and prepare him for the day when he would resume his entrepreneurial journey.

Chapter Eight

— ✑ —

Seven Years Later

OUTSIDE THE TEMPORARY CANVAS FENCING which cordoned off the new Temple, the city pulsated with activity in final preparation for the great festival. Tomorrow was to be the beginning of the great feast of dedication and the whole nation had gathered in Jerusalem to celebrate the christening of this most marvelous of shrines.

For as far as the eye could see the people of Israel were camped on the hills surrounding the city. From the deserts of the south to the mountains of the north they had come, bringing with them the choicest sheep and cattle from their herds for the great sacrifice. The date of the great celebration had arrived and the energy in the air was palpable in anticipation.

Efram strolled reverently in the open courtyard of the Temple, his footsteps echoing on the stone flooring. Except for the handful of priests applying a final coat of polish to the gold pilasters, the great new Temple was empty. He walked in silence and marveled at the magnitude of the beauty of the grand structure while reflecting on the seven-year journey he had taken at the side of his king.

For the duration, the entire kingdom had sacrificed as King Solomon focused his people on the building of this great Temple. Hundreds of thousands of man-hours, an immeasurable volume of gold, silver and bronze, and painstaking detail on every level had gone into the construction of this holy shrine, and now, it was completed.

This was the eleventh year of King Solomon's reign and he had led his people wisely and with integrity from the day of his coronation. Though still a young man his honor and fame resounded throughout the known world and the legend of his wisdom grew by the day. He led his nation in the ways and precepts of the Almighty and prospered beyond measure in all that he did.

To all it was evident that Jehovah had indeed touched the life of King Solomon. And young Efram Ben-Jared had walked beside his king for the past seven years and recorded all that he saw.

Efram stood for a moment admiring the architectural detailing of the great structure. In the distance he heard the familiar shuffling of sandals on the smooth stone flooring. He smiled as the sound approached and his father rounded the corridor and came into view.

"Magnificent, is it not?" said Efram to his father. "King David, God rest his soul, would have been proud to see all that his son Solomon has accomplished."

"I know the feeling well," said the elder Jared. "A father's greatest joy is to see his off-spring prosper and achieve and be honored." He smiled warmly to his son and the two men walked several more paces down the great colonnade. The father resumed the conversation after a moment of silence. "What now are your plans, my son?"

Efram glanced at his father with a look of puzzlement. He had not breathed a word of his plans to anyone but his wife and was surprised that his father seemed to know what was in his heart.

Efram replied after a slight pause. "Father, the time has come for me to resume the journey I am called to travel. My

dream to become a leader in commerce and trade has been rekindled and I am certain that now I am ready." The determination and
resolve of the young man radiated in his words.

"And why do you now believe that you are ready to succeed in such a competitive arena?" asked Jared. He knew the
answer, but wished to hear it from the mouth of his son.

"Since my ill-fated venture of seven years ago I have
searched myself to understand why it is that I tasted defeat.
During the same time I have studied our king and his ways, and
likewise the habits which have caused him to prosper. I have
observed the proverbs and principles he has practiced and have
recorded them on the parchment, as well as in my heart. These I
now have as a map for my journey and this will I use to guide me."

The elder Jared listened to the words of his grown son
before him and smiled. "Yes, I have known for some time," he said.
"I have watched with pride these past few years as your prominence has grown and it brings me great joy to see the humble, yet
dignified way you carry yourself. I observe how your colleagues
respect you and how the elders at assembly speak highly of you. If
you continue to walk in the ways of wisdom I have no doubt that
you will flourish in all that you do. But, my son," he paused
momentarily, "there is one thing you must never forget."

"Yes, father?" Efram waited with a sense of urgency made
all the more poignant by his father's increasing years.

"All great leaders, regardless of their chosen profession,
understand and practice the principle that I am about to share with
you. It is the only true way to earn lasting riches and respect."

The distinguished elder scribe hesitated, and then continued softy and deliberately to emphasize his words. "Seek never to

promote yourself, my son. Rather, seek only to serve. For anything in life you desire - be it riches, honor or influence - may be yours, if you focus your efforts on helping those within your charge *first* get what they desire."

Father and son were quiet for several minutes as they continued their tour around the glistening new shrine. With the profound words resonating in his mind Efram fought to control the emotion that welled within him. In what seemed to be the twinkling of an eye his beloved father had become an old man and Efram was acutely aware of the dwindling number of opportunities he would have to absorb the wisdom of this man who had guided him. Though others often repeated the wise sayings which they had memorized from the sacred writings, his father's words carried real truth and credibility: for upon them he had built his life.

Efram Ben-Jared silently placed his arm around his aging father's shoulder and vowed to himself that he, with the help of the Almighty, would confirm his father's creed in his own life as an example for the generations to follow...

CHAPTER NINE

—— ✎ ——

THE FIRST RAYS OF SUNLIGHT rose over the plains to the east and illuminated the outskirts of the city of Megiddo in the distance. Mahedi, the great merchant trader's chef, arrived on the patio with a pot of tea and a plate of fruits and sweet cakes for breakfast as the birds in the palm trees welcomed the new day with their chorus.

For nearly eight hours Darius had listened, spellbound, as Efram Ben-Jared shared the story of his life. The arrival of the chef in the first light of dawn reminded Darius that he and his elderly host had stayed awake the entire night. Oddly, Darius was not the least bit tired. Efram, though well advanced in years and unaccustomed to such late hours, was equally energized as he related the experiences of his life to his new young friend.

"And so," said Efram, "it was some thirty years ago, on the eve of the dedication of the great Temple, that I left the profession of the scribe and embarked upon my career as a merchant trader. In the intervening years since that night I have humbly attempted to follow the ways of my maker in all that I have endeavored and he has graciously allowed me to prosper."

"Yes," nodded Darius. "Your success is known throughout the land. And who is able to count the number of traders and vendors who have benefited from your mentoring? Even the children at their studies have knowledge of your acumen in commerce. The example of your life is unparalleled, and the Almighty has truly blessed your endeavors," said Darius sincerely. He then paused briefly as his compliments turned to puzzlement.

"Though I am troubled by one thing," continued Darius. "You transcribed with your own hand the proverbs and principles which guided our King Solomon during the early years of his reign, and these you used to guide you in your endeavors. But why did our king, whose wisdom inspired many of the proverbs, stray from these words of truth in his final years?"

"Ah, my young friend, you have astutely recognized the point of my story," said the elderly Efram. "And though your words are most kind regarding the success the Almighty has brought into my life, I believe the real lesson he would have us learn is from the examination of our king's life." The elderly man paused, he himself not fully comprehending the course King Solomon's life had taken in its latter years.

"You see, there are two critical intersections on the horizon of a man or woman's life," continued Efram after a moment of reflection. "One presents itself following a moment of failure, the other following a moment of success.

"The choices that we face in our moments of failure are the easiest: we have only to decide whether to press on or to give up." He edged forward in his chair to emphasize his words. "*But the choices that we face with our successes are far more subtle and potentially much more treacherous.* It was here, at the pinnacle of his success, that our King Solomon lost his way."

"How is it that a man's prosperity could be dangerous to him?" Darius asked quizzically of his host.

"Allow me to explain by illustrating the events which led to the apex of our king's success," said Efram.

"In the early years of his reign King Solomon did a masterful job of uniting the people of his nation behind the great and worthy mission first envisioned by his father David: the building and dedication of the Holy Temple in Jerusalem. Our people, essentially nomads since their exodus from Egypt nearly five hundred years before, were ready to establish a permanent holy place for their sacrifices and worship. Thus, they gladly rallied behind the king's vision and willingly gave of their gold, energy and effort to see it realized.

"The royal architects had advised King Solomon that the Temple would require enormous amounts of raw materials for its construction and an equal measure of laborers to do the work. Consequently, the king conscripted thirty thousand men from all of Israel and sent them to the forests of Lebanon to cut the massive timbers which would be required. The men of Israel, motivated by their desire to participate in the building of this most grandiose of shrines, believed their king's promises that the forced labor would last only for the estimated four years required to complete the holy shrine.

"Though it soon became apparent that the Temple would not be completed in four years, the men of Israel remained dedicated to the cause and continued in their labor, focused on the day when it would be finished.

"Finally, after seven and one-half years, the great Temple was completed. At what would later be referred to as the pinnacle of his reign, King Solomon declared a sabbatical for the workers and summoned all of Israel to the great festival of dedication for the magnificent structure. To a man, the people of Israel were awed. The great sacrifice had indeed been worth it.

"But," continued Efram, "it was not long after the Temple was completed that the king faced the first substantive test of his reign - and sadly, I must say, failed." He paused momentarily to pour a cup of tea for himself and his guest.

"Our king had ruled our nation for eleven years and had walked in the ways of wisdom from the time of his coronation. For this entire period the whole of his kingdom had been focused on one goal: to see the completion of the great Temple. Because of his faithfulness and adherence to the ways of the God of his fathers, King Solomon flourished in all that he did and his reputation had spread throughout Asia Minor, Mesopotamia and even to the kingdoms of the Far East.

"But as his stature among the nations increased," continued Efram, "so did his pride. Within a matter of months of completing the great Temple, King Solomon foolishly began to bask in the glory of the magnificent structure and determined that a king such as himself should live in a palatial complex befitting his newly acquired status as the wisest king on earth.

"To build his palace to rival all palaces King Solomon conveniently reneged upon his earlier promises and issued a tersely worded two-sentence edict that reinstated the forced labor law. With the stroke of a quill and nary a thought to the aftereffect of his action, the king ordered the men of Israel back to the forests and quarries and forced them to toil there for an additional thirteen years until his elaborate palace was completed.

"*Because of the king's growing sense of self-importance,*" emphasized Efram, "the great wisdom upon which his reputation had been built gradually began to ebb from him and his judgement became increasingly flawed."

"Was this alone the cause of our great king's undoing?" asked Darius.

"Unfortunately, my young friend, it was only part of the cause," replied Efram. "His destruction was hastened also by his lack of resistance to the temptations of this life. As his pride and ego grew, so did his appetite for pleasure and possessions.

"Early in his reign the prophets had warned our king to avoid taking a wife from the pagan nations of the world. Though our king had shown great respect for the word of the prophets until this point, he inexplicably chose to ignore this mandate and took the daughter of the king of an enemy nation as his bride. Soon, under the guise of forging strategic alliances with other pagan nations, he took wives from their countries as well. Without regard for the inevitable tragic consequences of his actions our king eventually appropriated some seven hundred women from foreign lands to join his marital harem.

"His blatant disregard for this and other laws of the Almighty gradually eroded his character and he soon lost touch with his people and the God of his fathers. As his wives and their worship of idols led him farther and farther astray he spiraled so deeply into depravity that today our nation is at the point of collapse and his own soul lingers at the entrance to the eternal abyss."

Efram shook his head in bewilderment and continued. "I ask you, if the great King Solomon - with the very hand of God upon his life from the time of his birth - can be led astray by his own pride and appetites, who among us is immune to the same danger?"

Darius silently nodded in agreement as he pondered the question posed by his host.

After a moment of quiet contemplation Efram concluded his remarks to Darius. "My friend, you are a young man who has earned a place of honor among our people. Your life is full of promise and I am certain that much success will come your way in the years ahead. Therefore, as you journey through this life carry these two essential truths with you always: first, in your moments of failure, choose to learn from your defeat and press on.

"And second, in your moments of success," the great merchant trader beseeched his young guest, *"walk humbly and guard your heart that pride and self-importance do not enter in. For these have ensnared more leaders than all other traps combined."*

For several minutes the younger man and the older man said nothing as they enjoyed the serenity that accompanied the arrival of the morning sun. In the golden light of the dawn they then clasped hands and embraced in farewell, both keenly aware and obviously pleased that the seeds of friendship had been planted.

Darius, deeply inspired by his encounter with the great man, broke the silence with an uncharacteristically forward request. "Teach me the laws of leadership, Efram," he beseeched his host with an earnestness that surprised even himself.

"Indeed, I shall," replied Efram with a contented, near prescient certainty in his voice. "I sense that our meeting was for some greater purpose and my spirit confirms that its time will be soon."

CHAPTER TEN

— ∞ —

IT WAS NEARLY THE MIDNIGHT HOUR by the time Darius completed the seventy-mile return trip from Megiddo to the outskirts of Jerusalem. With the exception of a few hours rest in Efram's guest quarters following their all night conversation he had slept precious few hours in the past two days and was exhausted. Unfortunately, a full night of sleep was not to be had on this night either.

As he neared the North Gate of the walled city Darius was startled by the amount of activity he saw ahead of him. Normally, all of Jerusalem would be asleep at this hour, except for the sentries who stood watch at their posts on the perimeter walls. But tonight a great commotion stirred and a multitude of people milled about. Upon closer examination Darius observed that many of the people bore the unmistakable signs of mourning: ashes upon their foreheads and outer garments that had been torn. At the moment of realization he also heard the anguished cries of the people ahead of him. *The king is dead! The king is dead! Our great King Solomon is dead!*

Darius maneuvered his horse and chariot through the great throng of mourners and made his way to the sentry's post just outside the North Gate. He was met by a young lieutenant who proceeded to tell him of the events of the past six hours. Within a matter of minutes a captain and two stone-faced guards emerged from the crowd and approached Darius' chariot.

"You are excused, lieutenant," said the captain to the young sentry who spoke with Darius. "And please see that this animal and carriage are returned to the royal stables at once." He directed his attention to an alarmed Darius. "Follow me, sire," he said as he led Darius through the crowd and toward the guard building some thirty paces inside the gate.

Darius could only imagine the worst as he walked in step with the somber guards on either side of him. *Prince Re'boam has apparently seized power,* he reasoned. *What is to be my fate? And what of the other council members? Are they also in custody?* He tried in vain to allay his fears as the uncertainty of the situation nearly overwhelmed him.

Upon arrival at the small stone building the captain posted the two guards at the outer door and led Darius into its interior. He then latched the wooden door behind them, removed his bronze helmet and motioned for Darius to be seated at the table.

"Please excuse the pretense of arrest, Master Darius," he then said to his guest, "but Prince Re'boam has decreed the imprisonment of you and the other council members and has demanded to be notified the moment of your return. However," he further explained, "I and others within the royal guard have been sympathetic to your efforts and cannot allow this to happen." Darius sighed his relief.

The captain continued. "Upon the news earlier this day of our King Solomon's passing, my trusted subordinates spirited the other council members away where they are secure in safe houses throughout the city. And I have for you an urgent message from General Nebo." The captain removed a note from his pouch and handed it to Darius.

Our council shall meet at the twelfth hour tomorrow eve at a place which shall be made known to you. You are in safe hands with our kind ally.

Darius folded the note and placed it in his leather attaché. There were many questions swirling in his mind, but unfortunately there was no one who could provide the answers. He simply would have to wait while the events of the immediate future played out.

"We should depart quickly," said the captain. "The prince's men shall come looking for you at once when his spies discover that your horse and chariot have been returned to the royal stables."

Darius hurriedly gathered his effects and followed the captain out of the small guard building. Assuming the formation of arrest the captain and his two lieutenants escorted Darius through the crowd and made their way toward the lesser traveled streets of the city. For the next half of an hour they walked, first one way and then another, in an effort to lose anyone who might have followed them. Eventually they arrived at a run-down inn somewhere in the southwest corner of Jerusalem.

The captain led Darius around the side of the building to a narrow alley way and, from there, to a non-descriptive door which led to a stairwell that bypassed the lobby. They entered and climbed the one flight of stairs to the boarding rooms on the second floor. Darius was given a small room and instructions to rest for the night. Additional information and further directions would arrive on the morrow.

After washing at the bowl and pitcher of water that were

situated on the bureau, he collapsed upon the bed, exhausted from the events of the past two days. Though his body ached for rest his mind refused to relax as the questions regarding the uncertainty of the future - his own and his nation's - engulfed him. After nearly an hour spent pondering the possible outcomes to the danger he faced, the rest which he craved finally arrived and he drifted off to sleep.

CHAPTER ELEVEN

—— ✢ ——

IN THE TWILIGHT BEFORE DAWN Darius was roused from his slumber to the sound of pounding on doors in the hallway outside his room.

"Open up," an angry voice shouted. "We are here on the king's business and will not be impeded." Judging by the heavy footsteps and number of voices it sounded to Darius as though eight or ten guards had arrived.

The prince's men have come for me. A rush of fear gripped him as his heart thumped nearly through his chest. From the sounds it appeared as though they were within four or five doors and would arrive at his within moments. He frantically gathered his cloak and sandals and struggled to move the large cedar chest from the foot of his bed to the doorway. He quickly reviewed his options for exit and discovered that the window was the only way out. After removing the thin wooden lattice he pushed out the shutters and was relieved to see that a trellis with vines extended from the ground to his second floor room.

He made his way down the trellis, grateful that his escape was concealed by three massive olive trees which grew in the courtyard below. Once on the ground he pulled the hood of his cloak over his head and headed for the market area at the city square to discover whatever news he could.

He kept a watchful eye on his immediate surroundings as he strolled nervously and as nonchalantly as possible through the great square. Though it appeared to be the beginnings of a normal morning of buying and selling, a sense of trepidation was reflect-ed on the faces of the shoppers and merchants which he passed by.

He continued to mill about for a few moments until he noticed a group of elderly men gathered for their morning bev-erage at a tea stall approximately one hundred paces to his left. *If I can get to them maybe I can hear of the latest news and rumors.* He casually but cautiously made his way through the crowd.

Not halfway to his destination, though, a great commotion arose and panic swept through the crowd as twelve royal guards dressed in full battle armor and mounted on black stallions arrived on the scene. Frozen in fear with the rest of the crowd as the cav-alry unit advanced, Darius counted at least six people who lay injured on the ground, trampled by the galloping horses.

A great hush fell over the crowd as the leader of the caval-ry unit raised his sword above his head. "King Re'boam has declared martial law effective immediately," he bellowed with great authority. "Every man and woman to their home at once. Any lin-gerers shall be arrested upon sight." For emphasis, the leader directed two of the guards to torch one of the small produce booths to his right. Amidst the screams and pandemonium the crowd frantically disbursed and scattered to their homes.

Darius stood amongst the chaos and fear pondering his next move as two hooded men silently approached him from behind. Before he was able to elude them the taller of the two men discreetly grasped his arm, while the other said "Come with us."

From the tone of his voice to the secretive nature of their dress, Darius interpreted the words as more of a command than an invitation and thought it wise to do as they said. *Besides*, he real-ized, *I've nowhere else to go.*

The unknown men led him for several blocks through the labyrinth-like streets of Jerusalem, with the pathways becoming increasingly narrow, until arriving at an old and apparently unoccupied warehouse in the spice traders district of the city. Darius was led into the building through a ventilation shaft at the rear alley. Once inside, the trio proceeded up a wooden ladder to a loft area above the main floor.

In the far corner of the dimly lit loft Darius observed a cot, as well as a bureau, a wash basin and assorted other items necessary for an extended stay. In the near corner was a small desk with a single chair. And on top of the desk was a parcel of some sort, wrapped in weathered canvas and bound by thin leather straps.

Darius was perplexed by this whole scenario. Though he'd gathered early in this relatively friendly abduction that his captors were not out to harm him, he had no clue to their intentions.

The shorter of the two men then directed Darius to be seated at a chair by the desk. He complied, yet was immediately staggered with shock as they removed their hooded cloaks: his abductors were none other than Jelor and Jabul, chief servants of Efram Ben-Jared.

In the instant before he was able to summon a response, movement in the darkened corner to his left caught his eye. He turned to see the great man himself emerge from the shadows. Darius sat in stunned silence as Efram drew near and began to speak.

"Greetings, my young friend. I shall delay my explanation for a moment until the surprise loosens its hold upon your reasoning." Jelor procured an additional chair and placed it across from Darius'.

"I trust that you will forgive the veiled nature of our meeting," said Efram as he was seated. "Considering the danger that exists, I thought it the prudent way to proceed."

Though visibly relieved, a bewildered look remained upon Darius' face. "Tell me what has occurred, Efram, that we should meet in such secrecy?"

"Though still a rumor, my sources suggest that Prince Re'boam seeks to try the council members for treason - and I am wanted, as well. I suspect that his fury is merely a show of his new found power and will soon fade; nonetheless, this safe harbor will allow you to endure the storm. This aside," Efram paused briefly, "I believe that your time here has been arranged for another reason." He glanced at the canvas-wrapped package upon the desk.

"Before I proceed with what I have planned," he then said pointedly, "I must know if your request when last we met was sincere?"

Darius nodded without hesitation. "My zeal to gain your knowledge has only grown. Teach me the wisdom you have gleaned, Efram."

"Then it shall be as you desire. Let us begin." Efram looked to Jelor, who gathered the package from the desk and handed it to him.

"Many years ago, at a time when my enthusiasm far exceeded my experience, I was given by our king a collection of proverbs on the art of influence. Though simple in their message and forthright in their motive, his inspired writings so moved me that I determined to apply them to every facet of my life.

"As the years progressed and my adherence to these principles brought prosperity to my endeavors, a few took notice and requested that I teach them. To my pleasant surprise I found much joy in the sharing of these truths and soon crafted from them a series of lessons for those in my profession to follow. Unknown at the time, my life's work had begun." He glanced again at the package. "The parcel that you see before us contains the summation of this work.

"I am old now," he said after a moment of reflection, "and must acknowledge that the time set aside for my purpose has concluded. As such, I have need of nothing except one thing: lest these words which have flowed from our maker through my pen are duplicated and disbursed, there is danger they will die with the one who set them to the page. Moreover, to carry them to my grave when their truths have brought such blessing would be selfish beyond shame. Therefore, I ask that you transcribe several sets of these teachings and secure them safely. For soon there'll come a season when the message may be multiplied." Darius instinctively nodded his agreement.

"Secondly, when your task is completed, you must resettle yourself beyond the reach of the prince's spies. When the fury of the present tempest has passed, quietly finalize your affairs in Jerusalem and make your way to the port city of Jaffa on the Mediterranean. There, in this bustling crossroads of many cultures, you will find abundant opportunity to establish yourself as a trader of goods and to apply the principles set forth in the writings. I shall supply you with just enough gold to open an account with Zamalo at my trading house by the docks." Efram again looked to Jelor, who removed a small pouch from his cloak and gave it to Darius.

"While it is well within my powers to set you at the helm over many and much," continued Efram, "such would only harm you; for true leadership - like success - must be earned by the one who seeks it." The intensity of his gaze reflected the gravity in his words. "Your struggles in this season are promised to be many. Shall I continue?"

"Yes," nodded Darius.

"Thirdly, as you begin your new endeavor, a time of study must adjoin it. It matters not the venture which you choose to embrace nor the number of those whom will follow in your steps, be it one, the many or the multitudes. The first signpost which points to leadership success reads the same for all: *to give direction, you must first seek it.* These teachings I bequeath you shall be the starting point for your journey." Efram handed the parcel to Darius, who received it reverently.

"The principles which inspired these proverbs have passed through the ages and emerged with their truths confirmed and intact," said Efram as he set forth his instructions. "Though a desire for prosperity has compelled you to learn, do not be tempted to rush through these pages at ravenous speed. The words are not intended to be devoured as if common fare at a table set for the gluttonous following a fast. They were neither given nor recorded in haste, therefore do not read them in such manner.

"Before any great truth will be learned, repetition, reflection and response are required for its weight to leave a lasting impression upon the memory of the reader. Thus," counseled the master, "you must develop the nightly habit of reading one selected passage from this collection and meditating upon its theme, be it Courage, Example, Servanthood or another. As you reflect upon the words, relate them to your past experiences and consider the response which is requested in your future. Then, to personalize the message and seal it within, close by reading aloud the parable

or self-affirming verse at the end of the passage. Do you understand the importance of establishing this habit?"

"Yes," replied Darius.

"Good. Arise on the morn which follows and read again
the selected passage in preparation for the coming day.
Throughout the day focus on its theme and seek situations to test
and prove its lesson. For it is only when you *apply* truth and not
just read it, does it become real to you and thus, influence change.
Then, at the end of your day before retiring, read a subsequent
passage within these writings in similar manner.

"Consequently, over the course of many days you will have
abided with each of the principles for one full day. But do not be
contented to cease your studies here, for your mind is liken to the
farmer's field: *it is only in the consistent and persistent application of nourishing waters will a great harvest come forth*.
Therefore, repeat this cycle for a second period of equal days and
continue yet again for as often as is needed for the letter and spirit of these teachings to root in your life.

"I must warn you, though," his fatherly advice grew cau-
tionary in its tone, "it is during this time that most would-be leaders grow impatient and weary of the effort. Yet you must remain
diligent, for to harvest the traits of character you will need *tomorrow*, you must plant with repetition the seeds of wisdom *today*. Are
you willing to commit to this course of action until the laws have
become as habit?"

"Yes," Darius replied quietly, yet with conviction.

"Very well then," continued Efram, "I shall leave you with
this final and most important of instructions." He leaned toward
Darius and emphasized his words. "*Seek and associate with those*

who share your desire for achievement - for they shall be the ones in whom your quest is made complete. Teach these proverbs to all who will receive them and equip them with a copy to go and do the same. In such manner alone will these writings have a chance to live on."

Efram rose from his chair and, in a gesture that signaled his confidence in the young man before him, held his farewell bow for a moment longer than was necessary.

"Your trials will be great," he said solemnly, "and we have no certainty that these teachings will survive to the benefit of those whom will follow. But I trust that He who has stirred my thoughts will inspire your labors, and keep them alive following our departure from this world.

"May your courage be equal to the challenge as you carry forth these words." He then turned and headed toward the ladder.

Efram Ben-Jared quietly descended from the loft as his servants followed closely behind. Darius watched in silence as they departed, then carefully removed the thin leather straps which secured the parcel. An odd yet comforting presence settled upon him as he gently unwrapped the loosely bound collection of parchments. He held them in his hands for a moment and was energized by the life force that seemed to resonate from within them.

An unexplainable sense of purpose immediately displaced his distress regarding the uncertain future. Despite the turmoil which threatened his world, this was to be his mission - and he knew it. He smiled and, with tears in his eyes, selected quill and ink from the holder on the desk. He then removed a fresh piece of parchment from the drawer and began to copy...

BOOK TWO:
The Proverbs

THE WRITINGS & ORATIONS OF
EFRAM BEN-JARED

— ∞ —

TEACHINGS
from the book of Wisdom,
for the pondering and preparation
of those who would lead.

MAY THE HEARER BE QUICKENED
to heed these words,
for the secrets of influence
dwelleth within.
Contemplate this counsel
ye seekers of wealth,
for the pathway to prosperity
is likewise revealed.

TO YOU WHO ARE SUMMONED
to spearhead a cause:
may your mind be opened
that your spirit be filled
to go forth with the power
to inspire the many.

BEHOLD AND BEGIN;
your time is upon you.

1
PROLOGUE

—— ∽ ——

A purpose has been granted unto all who walk the earth,
but only those who seize the opportunities which conceal it
will discover the road which leads to its fulfillment.

By the fact that you've enrolled in the school of self-improvement it is presumed that you seek the higher calling to your life. Upon this premise these teachings shall begin.

"...*A purpose has been granted unto all who walk the earth...*" Read again this statement and reconcile its words with the path on which you travel. Will the meaning that you seek be found if you continue? If yes, be commended and proceed on your quest. If no - and a longing for significance lingers in your thoughts - do not despair; for today is the day to redeem yourself with action by returning to the road which is readied for your steps.

Yesterday has departed; tomorrow is not promised;
all that remains is what you do with *now*.

Regardless of the failings or successes of your past, the sum of your experiences has prepared you to prosper in the endeavor now before you. All that you've done and all that you've endured has molded you for the mission which awaits your response. All that remains is to act, to work, to commit - and a leader of many you shall become.

And yet be forewarned. The call upon your life will not last forever and will fall upon the ears of another if you ignore its invitation. Do not succumb to the temptation to shun your assignment, nor postpone its acceptance to another day. For are you eternal that you might defer the appointed hour of your purpose forever? You are not.

The hours which are entered in the ledger of your life are of limited number and count off with increasing speed. Lest you rise and embrace the opportunity which beckons, the allotment of your days will dwindle to depletion and you will have lived without leaving a mark.

Your maker has designed for you a life of significance and placed within your grasp the plan to make it so. *The decision to accept it, though, is yours alone to make.* Act, and you will live to make a difference in the lives of many. Defer, and you will die without distinction; the seeds of your potential having sifted to the wind. Today, heed the call which whispers in your spirit and subdue its summons not a single second more. Today, put away the doubts which delay you and commence on the course which leads to success.

An unanchored ship will drift
if left to guide itself.

The passage toward your purpose is not without risk, for you embark upon your voyage with vision that is unclear and with questions that are many. How is it possible to sail with surety, you may wonder, when untold others before you - each with abilities far surpassing your own - have drifted from their course and wrecked upon the rocks of pride, greed and other self-induced disasters? Take comfort and be calmed, for your maker has provided the tools to steer you clear of these perilous cliffs. You have only to use them wisely and your course shall be followed to its completion.

Your thoughts have the power to guide you to greatness - or to deceive you to your demise.

When bolstered with prayer and the principles of truth, the internal compass known as THOUGHT is the chief device that is given to guide you; and the precision with which you direct it determines who you are and thus, whom you will become. As you have thought thus far, you are today. As you think from now, you shall one day be. This is the first Proverb - not of leadership - but of life: *As you think it, so shall it be.*

Liken to the ray of sunlight through the looking glass your thoughts care not upon which they are focused and will shine with intensity in whatever direction they are aimed. If you concentrate on fear and anxiety, in like manner shall you be led. If you focus upon nothing, you shall wander aimlessly upon the sea of mediocrity. But as those who achieve their greater purpose will attest, if you direct your thinking toward a worthy objective your mind will spur you to embrace and complete it.

Be careful to direct your thoughts to the end that you desire, for you will arrive exactly where you focus.

Do not allow unpurposed thoughts to determine your destination; rather, choose the destination and constrain your thoughts to the course which you have set. *As you think it, so shall it be.*

Today, picture in your mind the life that you desire and focus your thoughts that it might come to pass.

A leader's road to prominence requires many steps.
The wise are diligent not to miss even one,
while the anxious rush ahead and soon lose their way.

Wisdom stands at the pier and shouts its lessons to all who sail in search of success. Sadly, but one in a hundred will pause their vessel to listen. *"I am busy now,"* the ninety-nine say, *"surely I will stop later to hear your message."* Yet they do not understand that *later* means *never*.

They have ears but do not hear. And each time they pass by Wisdom and ignore the message their ears become increasingly dulled. Soon, the callings which lead the way to abundant living will be but a faint whisper, obscured by the noises of life. But this need not be your fate, for Wisdom, this day, has requested to join you. Receive it as a trusted companion and you will prosper.

Your lot is to lead and train others to do likewise, and today you embark upon the journey to this end. Acknowledge the greater purpose that exists for your life, embrace the endeavor which will see it come to pass, and *act* that its fulfillment shall be timely and certain.

Behold and begin, for your time is upon you.

AS YOU THINK, SO SHALL IT BE

~

Have your thoughts wandered aimless
like a boat upon the sea,
without plan or purpose
or a sense of destiny?
If so, this mental drifting
is the reason that you've stalled
and remain far and distant
from the port to which you're called.

Success for you has signaled,
with a passageway designed,
but its shore will not be found
until you fix it in your mind.
As the mariner his map,
your thoughts will be your chart;
if success shall be your end,
this must be your start.

Set your gaze and lock it
on the life that you seek;
visualize achievement,
its fulfillment, start to speak.
For 'tis only when your focus
is made sharp as the glass
will the goals that you've set
be made clear and come to pass.

So from here set a new course,
with your drifting left behind;
the life that you desire -
sear its picture in your mind.
For as you look ahead,
know this, of destiny:
As you think within your heart,
so shall it one day be.

2
RELEASE THE PAST

——— ⟨∞⟩ ———

To find the way forward you must first find the way to forgive.

Think for a moment upon the endeavor you have chosen and of those who have prospered on its path. Has anyone strolled to its summit of greatness, never to have made a mistake along the way? And of those whom will follow in their steps; will any arrive unaccompanied by error?

Think also of life and of the noble pursuits which make it worth living. Are there any among us who've not failed grandly many times in the quest? In truth, only three: *The timid soul who is terrified to try, the critical one who has never attempted, and the comfortable one whose dreams are too small.*

All who strive, who stretch, who reach for the golden ring will err and experience failure along the way. Therefore, be not ashamed of your mistakes; for 'tis better to be bruised as one who has tried and failed than to stand unsullied with the cowards and critics. When an error in judgement or action brings you low, rise and resolve to continue with your all....and try again.

There are those, however, whose pain from previous failings will not allow them to progress, for they find themselves chained to the memory. It is these to whom this lesson is addressed.

The only shame in failure
is to neglect to learn from it.

It is tempting to think of one's failings as disgraceful, with no redeeming value and to be forgotten at once. Yet know this: any attempts to forget will be in vain, for the memory is liken to a reservoir that retains all, and will not allow it.

Lying dormant in the recesses of the subconscious it comes to life in the moment of opportunity, gleefully sending forth reminders of your mistakes to overwhelm you with fear and doubt. *"Don't you recall your defeat in a similar endeavor?"* it will whisper at the moment you're inspired to attempt a great feat. *"Do not even try,"* it will convincingly scoff, *"for you may fail again."*

To forget a mistake before seeking its lesson
condemns you to repeat it and thus relive its pain.

To defeat the memory's might you must be liken to the wise man who faces his failings and seeks the instruction within. While not dwelling on his failure, neither does he flee when its memory returns. So too must be your plan. When a memory from your past revisits to restrain you reflect upon your actions which brought about the mistake, remedy what you can and pledge by heaven's grace that you will not repeat it.

To learn from an error is to gain experience;
to forgive yourself the error, freedom.

It shall not be enough to simply learn from your mistakes: you must also forgive them. Why? The unforgiveness of self is liken to a prison whose walls grow closer by the day. Unchallenged, its captivity can last a lifetime (and often does) for those who refuse to forgive and break free.

Proficient in the art of restriction it rules the captive from within by commissioning the sentries of Guilt and Remorse to enforce its power. "*The errors of your past are permanent*" these foot soldiers of unforgiveness will tempt you to believe, "*and will imprison you the rest of your days.*"

When these taunts of regret grow loud and you find it difficult to pardon the mistakes you've made, consider this: Does your maker keep a record of your wrong following your sincere repentance? No. Does he mock you with reminders of your past defeats? Most certainly not. Why, then, should you be so cruel? You must not. While not excusing the unpleasant consequences of the decisions you've made nor begging for relief from them, you must silence the reminders which prohibit your advance.

The key to your freedom is forgiveness - and you will find it when you start with yourself. It is not a key of iron nor of stone and yet its strength is sufficient to undo the strongest of restraints. Its liberating power is supreme yet it turns on the smallest of words. Utter these words when you fear that your mistakes will forever follow and the irons which bind you to them shall begin to loosen. "*Let it go.*" These are the words which will secure your freedom. Use them, and be set free.

If the memory of lost riches fills you with remorse, forgive the failed gamble and reap its shame no more. If poorly made decisions render you motionless with fear, pardon the wrong choices and decide to move ahead. And if the reminder of missed opportunity overwhelms you with regret, forgive the inaction and double your efforts in the venture before you.

On the road to reach your potential
an unforgiving spirit will only slow you down.

Lastly, you must also forgive those who've wronged you, for the weight of this burden will impede you where you're headed. Regardless of the pain which you carry from another, leave it to your maker to convict the one who caused it. Today, remove its heavy yoke and bear it no more. Let it go.

The journey to fulfill the call upon your life is liken to the journey of a thousand miles: it begins with a single step. Today, free yourself from that which holds you back. Take the first step...and forgive.

RELEASE THE PAST

~

This is a parable
from the days of old
'bout the memory of the past
and the power that it holds.
Applicable to all,
its message is profound;
for each of us has something
from our past that keeps us bound.

Our story thus begins
with a young man who was driven
to find his maker's purpose
for the life that he'd been given.
In search of his destiny,
he traveled and was led;
an unknown path he journeyed,
then he saw her up ahead.

She was beautiful and sweet
he could tell from afar,
and she glowed with the light
of the bright and morning star.
He tried to move in closer,
but she vanished like the wind;
who was this lovely lass,
and from where had she been sent?

As he watched her run away
he saw a string around her thumb,
and was puzzled by this thread
which pulled her back from where she'd come.
Enchanted, yet perplexed,
his interest had been piqued;
tomorrow he'd return -
her acquaintance he would seek.

Bright and early did he venture out
to see what he could see;
he made his way into the woods,
once again, there was she.
On the path she lingered briefly,
then off without a trace;
but one thing he was certain:
she'd a smile upon her face.
She retreated back from where she'd come,
back to his path he roamed;
though again, he was puzzled
by the thread which pulled her home.
This is strange, so he thought
as his heart began to yearn;
*I'll re-visit on the morrow
and I pray that she'll return.*

The next day in the forest
he feared that she was gone;
then suddenly she came to him,
as if she had been drawn.

Tho' surrounded by the beauty
of the nature and the trees
the sweetness of her spirit
was all that he could see.

Her face he took within his hands,
her mouth he softly kissed;
his life he'd searched and sought,
but this magic he had missed.
From the moment he first saw her
something deep inside him stirred;
to the still voice he listened,
"She's the one," is what he heard.

They spent the afternoon
hand in hand, midst the trees;
their laughter and their words
flowed abundant and with ease.
They pleasantly discovered
that their goals were much the same:
to serve their maker, seek his plan,
and lead others to his name.

As the daylight turned to dusk
and it was time to say good-byes,
he kissed her once again
and looked deep into her eyes:
"I do not mean to pry,
but the thread, what is it for?"
"It reminds me of my past," she sighed,
"and binds me even more."

Her pain was very clear
and had bound her far too long,
for something from her past
would not allow her to move on.
"If you'll meet me every day," he vowed,
"I'll bring these things with me:
kindness, patience, sharing -
maybe one will set you free."

So in the woods they daily met,
their spark became a glow;
yet still she clutched onto her thread
and would not let it go.
Her destiny was calling,
but she could not seem to find
the courage nor forgiveness
to leave her past behind.

Then one day the young man
left a note upon a tree;
it broke his heart to do it,
but it's the only way, you see.
For he'd sought his maker's voice
and the answer was quite clear:
*"The future is restricted
if the past remains too near."*

His affection had not changed,
there was nothing that she lacked;
but they could not move forward
while she remained held back.

A journey for them waited
and he knew it to be so;
but the girl could not depart
until her past she would let go.

So to those who are held captive
by what happened long before,
release whatever binds you,
to hinder nevermore.
And when your purpose finds you
you'll rejoice that you are free
to embark upon the journey
that will lead to destiny.

3
CHARACTER

———— ✺ ————

Build this before your empire.

As with all the great cities built to stand for the ages Jerusalem is established on a bedrock of stone. The outer wall which protects it is likewise constructed, for the footings that support it have been set to such a depth that it cannot be moved.

But what would happen if the plans for its foundation called for stones that were cracked? Or were it constructed with a base inadequate to carry its load? And what of the cities which might copy its design, unaware of the flaws concealed within? As sure as the sun will rise, each would collapse. Maybe not today nor tomorrow, but the downfall of all would be certain and inevitable.

And so shall it be in the building of your character. You may rise to a position of leadership based upon charisma or personality - and indeed succeed for a season - but such unstable stones are not sufficient to sustain you. If you are to endure through the challenges which will come and emerge with a character worthy of replication, your life must be established on a foundation that will last.

Integrity is the bedrock upon which character must be built; honesty with self, the first stone to set in place.

Do not bargain with life by coasting on talent or relying upon charm to reduce the payment required for success. Though such gifts have value they are often misused by the short-sighted to avoid sacrifice. If you are blessed with talent in abundance or skilled in the art of charm, do not deceive yourself and others by hiding behind your gifts to conceal your unwillingness to work. For, as many have discovered too late, the cost of your discount will be great and soon subtracted from your character.

Anything of lasting value requires, no, *demands*, that the price be paid in full before its benefit can be savored. Though talent alone may propel you to the summit, you will not be allowed to remain; for your conscience (and others) will quickly remind you that you did not pay the price which was necessary to get there.

Cheat by avoiding sacrifice
and you swindle only yourself.

There are no shortcuts in the construction of character. Though the price for building it may seem expensive today, to correct its flaws tomorrow following a failure will cost even more. From this day forth be honest with yourself and pay with gladness whatever price is demanded for success in your endeavors.

It is likewise essential to be honest with those whom you lead; for how can others have trust in your vision if your words speak not the truth?

You are not a king and have not the authority of commandment; thus the power of your persuasion rests squarely upon the truthfulness of your word. Exaggerate your claims or offer up excuses for your unkept promises and others will soon raise a skeptical brow to all that you say. But seek and speak truth in all that you endeavor and the integrity of your word shall be revered as if royal.

Tact is the velvet hammer which softens the blows of truth that is hard.

You must be sensitive when your people approach you for your honest counsel on a matter of importance; for though they request the truth, it may be uncomfortable, even unpleasant to their ears. But unpleasantness is not an acceptable reason to withhold its good, for truth is liken to the healing powders of the physician: though at times displeasing and momentarily discomforting, nevertheless necessary in order to reap the benefits of its power.

Sprinkle the truth with equal measures of tact and love, but speak it nonetheless in all situations to those who seek it. For that which is true, while not always palatable, is always profitable.

When asked by those in your charge, *"How far must I journey to reach the summit of success?"* Reply in truthfulness that success is a decision, not a destination; therefore, *decide* to reach it and one most certainly will, regardless of the steps required.

If questioned, *"Will the road be difficult and lined with discouragement?"* Reply with honesty that it will be, for sacrifice and setback are sure to accompany their travel. Yet encourage them to welcome these companions of adversity; for adversity, once overcome, seasons the trip and sweetens the arrival.

And if queried, "*What is the ultimate purpose of my journey?*" Reply that a life of significance is the goal; yet, like happiness, it comes only by service and never by seeking. Through the integrity of your example encourage them to set aside their seeking and begin to serve.

The height of your stature will never
exceed the depth of your compassion.

If integrity is the foundation of a leader's character, then compassion is the first pillar which must be erected upon its base.

If you take great pains to construct your dwelling but neglect the building of your family, your home will fall and your life will be for naught. If you preach with passion to the masses yet turn away the pupil who's fallen behind, the words of your instruction will soon lose their power to inspire. And if you command thousands yet have no concern for the soldier who is down, your victories will eventually be savored alone.

Never become so proud or arrogant or impatient with another's lack of progress that your compassion for him is lessened. Though your focus remaineth firm keep your heart tender toward those whom you lead and they will know that you care.

Give away what you need
and it will return to you multiplied.

A leader with a generous spirit will find that he lacks for nothing.

One of the greatest of our maker's laws is that we must first sow into the lives of others that which we hope to receive. If gold is what you seek you must begin to share the little that you have. If prosperity is your goal you must give of yourself to help others prosper first. And if a life filled with love is your hope and desire, you must first love those whose lives link with your own.

Henceforth, share of your gold to help those who have none; for the man or woman who gives generously shall prosper with abundance. Labor with the goal that others succeed; for he who builds another likewise builds himself. And give freely of yourself to those whom you love; for such is the well from which happiness is drawn.

Be generous with all that you have and you will rejoice as it returns to you a hundred-fold.

The final pillar in support of your character must be COMMITMENT; for how can others follow your steps with conviction if you are not committed to the cause that you proclaim?

Many among us speak eloquently and passionately of commitment, but in truth, have confused it with effort. And while effort is a worthy component of any endeavor, it is not equal to commitment.

Effort rallies many with noble words and passion, but commitment is what remains when the crowds have disbursed. Effort exerts itself until it cannot go on; commitment works through the pain until the job is done. Effort says "*I will try*" and gives its best; while commitment says "*I will do*" and gives its all.

Let your commitment to your cause be evident to all by your refusal to falter when your passion has faded. Beginning this day strike the word 'try' from your speech and replace it with 'do'. No longer try your best, but in all, do *whatever it takes* to complete the task at hand.

Finally, commit yourself to the matters which define your life and be unyielding in your conviction and dedication to them. To your family, commit your love and guide them unceasingly with the same. To those within your charge, commit your support and lead them with encouragement as they grow. And to your maker, commit your every step so that he might lead you on the path which is prepared for you.

The building of your character is a lifelong endeavor. Be unwavering for the duration in your commitment to its construction.

CHARACTER

~

The deception of self
is the worst of all lies,
for it holds back our growth
and limits our rise.
We're convinced that we're building
an honorable life
but continue to live
in a way that's not right.

Yet if the foundation
we build is not strong,
our character will crumble
when storms come along.

Two lives do we live,
in discord, do we fight,
while the turmoil inside
tells us something's not right.
We have an ideal
of whom we should be,
but the falseness within
restrains destiny.
We may change for a moment
when crisis comes near,
yet when crisis has past,
old paths do we veer.

We're but fooling ourselves
and causing our strife,
and prolonging - or missing -
God's plan for our life.
All he wants is what's best
when he's placed on our trail
the trials that will test,
and our strength, to unveil;
but we shun what is hard
and we don't comprehend
that we're harming ourselves
when his rules do we bend.

We may fool those who follow
for a while, it may seem,
but soon they will learn
that our words do not mean
what we say that they do,
for our lives don't agree
with the front that we show
and pretend it to be;
and then we'll have lost
their trust and concern,
and they will be gone....
to never return.

So from now, humbly vow
to be honest and true
in your words and your thoughts
and in all that you do.
Remove your disguise
and take off your mask,
so no longer will those
who follow you ask:
"What's their character like?"
For the truth will be plain,
since your words and your life
will be one and the same.

4

VISION

————— ❧ —————

Focus on the dream, not the distractions.

As the oil gives life to the flame and the flame to the fire, your dream is what gives power to your plan. And it is your dream that will carry you when your body is weak, your determination is depleted and your people have deserted.

Soon, if not already, setbacks such as these will occur and you must give an answer when the voice within wonders loudly: *"Why should I continue when such trials persist?"* This much is certain: only when your dream is bigger than the challenge to it will you find the reason to press on and through.

A dream is but a wish until is written down.

If you have not yet done so, cease what you are doing and write a clear and concise description of your dream upon the parchment, as well as the date by which you plan to achieve it. *Do this now*, for until your dream is written upon the parchment it will not transfer to your heart. And until it transfers to your heart it is only a wish and will not become reality.

Also post a description of your dream within your dwelling, that you might see it day and night. Likewise carry it within your carriage, as reminder that your dream has the power to transport you from your present circumstance. And lastly, carry it in your cloak next to your heart as reminder that your dream provides the beat to which you march.

As your dream becomes crystallized you will set in motion the force that will move you to accomplish great things. It matters not if you seek to increase your stature, prosperity for your family or an improved lot in life, for the principle is the same:

Power is released when the purpose is clear.

With an energy that comes from knowing where you're going you will no longer wander through life with goals that are vague or with plans that are small; for these serve only to propel the mediocre farther down their path. Neither will you be content with sustenance, shelter and a comfortable existence as the principal purpose for your toils; for such things, though important, are unable to satisfy the created need within you to grow, to stretch, to achieve.

From this day forth *dream and think big;* and the once grand plans which inspirited your youth will return with vigor. Today, rise from the rut of recent years, dust off the dreams which inspired your past and live out your days enlivened with purpose.

As your dream grows and becomes a part of your being you must protect and defend it, as if it were gold, for you will encounter many along the way who will seek to steal it from your grasp. If you are to succeed you must acquaint yourself with these enemies of your dream and become aware of their wiles and their weaponry.

Opposition is promised to those with a purpose.

DISTRACTION will likely be the first foe who will seek to keep you from your life's purpose. As such, be wise when dealing with this enemy for Distraction is among the most clever and cunning of the adversaries you will meet.

Like the wisest of warriors it knows better than to attack your dream head on, for surely you would see through its ruse and effectively counter. No, Distraction seeks only to *delay* you and will tempt you to focus your efforts on other worthy endeavors. For it knows that if you will pause for a short while to work on other things, other things will soon pull you from your primary path.

Thus, when the journey to your dream is momentarily interrupted by the obligations of life, fulfill your duties with a cheerful heart; but remain focused upon your dream and do not succumb to Distraction.

And who is the second ne'er-do-well you will surely encounter on your journey? It is none other than COMFORT.

Like the first enemy, Comfort is most subtle in its attack and will lull you into mediocrity if you remain unaware of its tactics. Comfort cares not if you experience a moment of success or a moment of failure; a moment of elation or a moment of discouragement - its refrain is the same. "*Stop for a moment and rest,*" it says, "*you have labored hard and you deserve it.*" For it knows that if you pause - either to rest or to rejoice - your momentum will halt.

Thus, when you are tempted to relish in the small victory of a moment or to pause with pity in the face of temporary defeat, focus your mind upon your dream and press on. And Comfort will not hold sway.

Acquaint yourself also with COMPARISON, a close cousin to Comfort and an equally crafty enemy of your dream. Comparison will typically arrive in your moments of setback and discouragement and will attempt to divert your gaze to those around you who have no dream. *"Why struggle so hard?"* it most likely will say, *"your present lot is quite good compared to this one, or to that one."*

When you are attacked by this foe remind yourself that Comparison never directs your attention to one who has succeeded beyond you; only to those who remain at your level or below. Remind yourself also that your maker has endowed you with talents, gifts and a purpose unique to you and does not chart your headway against your colleagues. Neither, then, must you. There is but one thing you need compare and that is your progress of today with your potential of tomorrow. And this will spur you to press on toward your dream.

The first leg of a journey is often traveled alone.

There are many other enemies of whom you must be aware, but there is one that strikes closer to your heart than all the rest. This enemy uses fond recollections from days gone by as its principal weapon and enlists Well Meaning Friends to deliver the attack.

On the road toward your dream you will learn that many of your loved ones do not wish to travel with you; for it seems that Comfort, Comparison and other such hindrances have securely bound them to their present station.

"You've changed," many of them will say. *"Why do you no longer join us in the activities of old?"* Sadly, a few will even ridicule your desire for an improved lot in life.

Though your loved ones' lack of understanding is troubling, this simple phrase from the wise men of ancient offers explanation for their misguided comments:

> The nail that raises its head above the others
> is the one that gets pounded down.

Thus, accept that your loved ones are comfortable in their present state, and that their comments merely unmask their desire that you remain with them. But this you cannot do, for your maker has birthed within you new life in the form of your dream and you must press on. Be thankful for fond memories of the past and visit them on occasion, but do not succumb to the temptation to dwell there.

Encourage your friends to join you on the adventurous road to the future, yet know that most will not; and some, in their ignorance, will attempt to thwart your efforts. To all, remain a friend, but do not allow their refusal to journey with you alter your destination or determination.

The final foe you must overcome is the one with which you are most familiar - and the one with the potential to be your greatest ally - for it is yourself.

For it is SELF, in the form of doubt, that will be the most powerful force you will face. Your other enemies are worthy adversaries, but at best, can only pull you from your path. You, and you alone, hold the power of life or death over your dream. Do not give in to this power, but harness it to your advantage.

When you become discouraged, think of your dream and press on. When you are afraid, think of your dream and gather courage. When you are tired, think of your dream and be refreshed. And when you are tempted to quit, think of your dream and double your efforts. From this day forth acknowledge your dream as the fuel for your spirit and it will propel you past the plagues of doubt.

Lastly, though you protect your dream as if it were gold and repel the attacks of those who would steal it, what shall be done if its fire becomes doused and no longer burns with intensity in your breast?

Humbly pray to your maker to revive it, renew it, or spark within you another that cannot be put out.

The Power of the Dream

~

When at first I began
I knew not what to do,
all I knew was that I wanted
something more than what I knew.
I stumbled and I struggled
as I tried to share my plan,
but they did not care to listen
nor even try to understand.
Then one day it came to me,
the answer, and I beamed;
'til then I had not focused
on a goal, much less a dream.
So I stopped where I stood
and my dream I defined;
for the first time I had purpose
and a point to fix my mind.
All at once I started doing
what took a week, in but a day;
my life now had direction
and my dream propelled the way.
Those close to me began to see ·
a change in how I fared,
and they wished to look again
at the plan that I had shared.
So I spoke to them with passion
of the vision in my heart
and many were inspired
to join in and be a part.

Now we labor side by side
with our eyes upon the prize,
each focused on our dream,
with purpose in our lives.
And tho' the path is hard and its obstacles impede,
we press on with persistence,
for someday we'll be free.

5

PERSEVERANCE

——— ✍ ———

The road to your success began when you chose it. Stay on it.

In life, the trails which lead to the pinnacle of achievement are as numerous and diverse as those who set out to reach it. Yet all who arrive, having prospered in their quest, share this in common: *each selected a path at the start of their journey and persevered on its course until the goal was reached.*

As you forge ahead on the road to your dream, decide, above all, that you will persevere on the path that you've selected. For as equally as important as the route which you have chosen *is your determination to remain on your chosen route 'til the end.*

To reflect with pride upon a job well done requires that you first complete it.

Success has many ways of testing the commitment of those who profess to seek it. Therefore, be prepared when the initial enthusiasm for your dream or endeavor begins to wane, for such is the moment that you will be tempted to abandon your undertaking and pursue another. *"This venture is more difficult than planned,"* the voice of discouragement likely will say. *"Forsake this road for one that is easier."*

Resist this desire to quit - and press on; for, if in the midst of this challenge you hasten to embrace the next venture, you will surely abandon it in a moment of weakness when the third one has beckoned. Perceive this impatience as but a test of your commitment, and persevere.

He who jumps from one endeavor to another, trying all, succeeds at none.

Beginning this day pledge to finish what you start, and start by acknowledging that ample opportunity exists where you are. Remove from your mind all thoughts of quitting, of seeking a better route, or of starting again elsewhere, and replace them with images of your endurance, persistence and tenacity. Whatever your desires for prosperity or prominence, know this: *you can get there from here, but you must persevere.*

Let not your eyes wander to the new and untested ways which promise an easier road to the fulfillment of your dream. When the enticing invitation of a new endeavor beckons, redouble your commitment to the venture you have chosen and repeat these words:

'I will stay this course
until I've prospered or perished.'

Though seemingly extreme to the faint of heart, this is the magical mantra that carries the power of completion upon its syllables. With repetition and conviction this phrase will soon become as natural as the drawing of air into your lungs. Make it your motto when you're tempted to abandon your road for another, and steadfast, you will remain. "*I will stay this course until I've prospered or perished.*"

Half done is still undone.

Moreover, be not liken to the sculptor who begins a work yet sets it aside before completion, unable to see the masterpiece hidden within. Though he discards the half-chiseled block of granite as worthless, the masterpiece is there nonetheless, waiting to emerge, *if only he would finish what he started.*

As with the sculptor, how many times have you been but a stone's throw from greatness, only to cease your efforts in a moment of frustration or fatigue? It matters not; but let this be no more. For until you complete the work you've begun, *the work begun in you will remain incomplete.* The venture set before you was presented for a reason; persevere, and the masterpiece that is your life will soon emerge. Press on.

Activity is not equal to Accomplishment.

As you develop the habit of perseverance you must also train yourself to delay the gratification of the reward until the objective is reached. Do not cheat yourself and those within your charge by rewarding *activity* instead of accomplishment, for sadly, this premature awarding of the prize will serve a dually detrimental effect. Not only will the negative habit of incompletion be reinforced, but the reward will not be able to be savored; for you and those who follow will know that it was not fully earned at the time it was bestowed.

Effort and work are essential to the completion of an objective and deserve a measure of merit; but these, alone, are not the desired result and therefore not to be rewarded on the same level with accomplishment.

Stated similarly, is the wreath of honor bestowed upon the runner who begins the race or to the one who finishes? Is an audience with the king granted to the warriors who begin the battle or to those who return when victory is won? The answer is simple: the effort of those who embark upon the challenge shall deserve a corresponding measure of recognition; but the ultimate prize of honor must be reserved for those who persevere and accomplish the objective.

In such manner, instill within yourself and within those whom you lead the proper correlation between effort, accomplishment and reward. Fix within your mind the goal for which you strive and discipline yourself to delay the gratification of its reward until the goal is reached. In doing so you will savor it all the more, secure in the knowledge that you persevered through the challenge until the objective was attained.

The journey to complete the call upon your life has begun. Lash your sandals firmly on the ship that you have boarded and resolve to sail its course to the end.

◢◣

THE PARABLE OF PERSEVERANCE
~

Two young travelers ventured up the narrow mountain track
and vowed to one another there would be no turning back.
They focused on the pinnacle and promised not to stop,
for none who'd gone before had ever reached the very top.

The first young man determined this would be his claim to fame,
for the multitudes would cheer him and bring honor to his name.
But the second man decided he would conquer this great hill
just to prove to self his strength and the power of his will.

So the two men started out, full of promise and of zest;
but soon, the path grew harder and their will received a test.
The first young man had not prepared his mind for such a task;
"Could they stop for just a while?" to the other he soon asked.

The other, who was stronger, agreed to his request;
but he knew they must press on, lest they tarry in their rest.
For he knew the greatest danger when one undertakes a cause
is to stop when things get difficult and thus, momentum pause.

They went back to the journey once their strength had been renewed;
each focused on exactly why this goal he had pursued.
The first man had set out seeking honor and acclaim,
while the purpose of the second man was growth, not personal fame.

His motive had been pure when he'd started on this quest;
recognition he'd not sought, only challenge and the test.
He'd sought not fame nor glory, nor medals nor awards;
for he knew that challenge conquered is the greatest of rewards.

The one who'd sought acclaim began to tire and to wane,
for his reason was not strong enough to overcome his pain.
Yet the one who'd sought the challenge gathered strength with every step;
powered by his goal and that his vow to self be kept.

As they pressed on toward the pinnacle a lookout point appeared;
would they try to reach the summit, or be content to cease right here?
For the view from here was marvelous, there'd be no shame to stop;
besides, they were quite tired, and still a long way from the top.

A decision was thus needed and each pondered in his heart,
"Is it really that important to complete what I have started?"
While the first man paused to focus on his weakness at great length,
the other chose to persevere, and focused on his strengths.

And so their roads diverged, from here they parted ways;
one chose to end his quest, one chose a trail to blaze.
The first man, self-defeated, chose to settle for the view;
while the second stayed the narrow road, resolved to see it through.

He pushed himself to conquer this most difficult of paths,
and fought to reach the top, though it took all that he had.
Then at once he saw it and his pain quickly fled,
for the goal that he had sought rose to greet him straight ahead.

As he stood atop the mountain where no one had gone before,
he forgot about the struggle, to remember nevermore.
His challenge was now conquered, what he'd started was now done;
from now he'd but recall the personal pride at victory won.

And when he reached the bottom, at the crowd, was he amazed;
seems they'd gathered in great numbers for his feat, to cheer and praise.
Not only had he finished what he set out to attain;
but tribute came his way, along with honor and acclaim.

And somewhere in the crowd was the first man, with regret;
for he knew if he'd but pushed himself, the goal, he would have met.
But now it was too late - the chance for greatness he had spurned -
forever he would wonder if to him it would return.

So to those who face a challenge and are tempted to give in,
stay the course, persevere, and let not the challenge win.
For when your road is conquered you'll be proud that you had stayed...
for 'tis then you'll have discovered just exactly what you're made.

6
RELATE-ABILITY

—— ∽ ——

*The pathway to success refuses any traveler
who attempts to walk alone.*

Beneath the great press by the olive grower's bins is a vat
which collects the precious oil for market. The bins will overflow
with a harvest of plenty when the season of gathering has reached
its conclusion, yet will this fact alone insure a great yield? It shall
not. Though the olives that will pass through the press are many,
how much of the oil would pour into the vat were the pressman's
funnel no larger than a hollowed reed? A few drops, at best, while
the bulk would rush by and be lost upon the ground. Conversely,
how much of the valuable oil would be collected if the pressman's
funnel were as large as the vat below? Indeed, nearly all.

In your past efforts to draw others to your cause have you been
liken to the pressman who uses the hollowed reed? If so, how many
prospects and potential confidants have unwittingly been turned
away because your actions and perceptions would not permit their
entrance?

If the opening to your circle of fellowship is restricted by your
self-centered view of the world, you will succeed in attracting to
your fold a mere fraction of those whom you'll chance to meet.
Were you called to be a scholar or a contemplative sage you could
labor in seclusion with no need to draw another; but you are not:

To succeed in the journey you have chosen
you must gather to your caravan a multitude of many.

How, then, shall you master the mystery of attraction? And what will compel great numbers to join you? The answer shall be found neither in the force of your persuasion nor in the nobleness of your purpose, *but in the level of your ability to relate to others*.

Were your giftings and talents superior to all, still you would fail if you neglect this truth. But learn to relate to all manners of men and success (and the masses) will follow your cause.

And how will you acquire proficiency in this skill? Must you labor to learn some ancient technique, or perhaps seek wisdom from a modern day master? Neither! - for all that you need was bequeathed you at birth in the form of your sight, your hearing and your speech. You need only to correct your usage of these senses, and the ability to relate will be imparted unto you.

So must you begin. No longer use the gift of your vision to focus on the flaws and frailties of another. Search instead for the virtue within him and bring it to light for all the world to see.

Never pay attention to the whispers of gossip, nor allow your ears to hear words that slander or diminish. When the idle or the agitators commence their hurtful chatter, always speak up for the one who is maligned and sing of their qualities to all whom will listen.

As for those whom you love, you must nurture and affirm, ever mindful of the power that your tongue wields within it. Never must you criticize nor crush a tender spirit, but with gentleness and patience correct their wayward steps. Seek always to build them with assurance and support, for such is the base from which their confidence may soar.

As for those whom you lead, bolster with encouragement all efforts toward their goal, regardless of their skill or the rate of their advance. Words that discourage must not pour from your mouth, nor any speech that dampens another's dream or desire. If one has a vision to improve his lot in life, offer what you have to help see it come to pass.

As for those whom you seek to entice to your cause, never must you pressure if they share not your passion, for such serves only to push them away. Instead you must labor for a season without them, trusting that the seeds of opportunity that you planted will return a great harvest on some future day.

To reach another, you must reach out to them
where they are.

With compassion the new lens through which all must be viewed, never again scoff at the beggar in the street nor turn with contempt from his outstretched hand of need. Instead, remember the ancient words of this prayer and silently repeat them when you're tempted to condemn: *There, but for the mercy of my maker, go I.* Regardless of the choices which have led him to his plight, see him as a brother lost and help him right his way.

No longer must you view yourself as superior to any, for though prosperous or poor, will your bones not return unto the same pile of dust? Never walk so tall to think that you can never stumble nor esteem yourself as wise and incapable of error. All forms of arrogance and conceit must be banished from your mirror, for such blinding self-deceptions distort your sense of worth.

Neither must you draw attention to your strengths nor boast of your talents that others might be awed. From this day forth dedicate the usage of the gifts you've been given for one purpose only: *to stir within others an awareness of their own.*

The creator has endowed each soul with potential and asks of you to see it in whomever you shall meet. With this simple truth the masses will receive you and the cause you've embraced. Without it you will flounder, even with those whom you love. From this day forth you must view every person in only one way: not as they have been or as they are, *but as how they were created to be.*

For when you view your fellow man through the eyes of our maker compassion and humility will flow from your heart.

And many will draw near to discover the source.

RELATE-ABILITY

~

Many times with friend or stranger
with impatience I have erred
by attempting to enlist them
before proving that I cared.
Full of fervor and of zeal,
I took no interest in their plight,
and pressed them for commitment
long before I'd earned the right.
Why am I not growing?
What secret have I missed?
What must I improve
if their help I'm to enlist?
How many have I pushed away
because I took no time
to listen to their dreams
before forcing on them mine?
Other times have I not recognized
one's emptiness or pain,
and spurred them for more effort,
focused only on my gain.

Though my call to arms be noble,
even grand beyond compare,
others won't respond
if, for them, I do not care.
So from now I will correct
my approach and appeal,
halting all pressure,
even tempering my zeal.

With empathy, I will listen,
and resist the urge to speak;
the perspective of another
at all times will I seek.
For when my first concern
is for another's point or pain,
'tis then I'll earn respect
and their trust, begin to gain.
Such is the only way
my circle will expand -
I must shine the focus off myself
and on my fellow man.
For 'tis only when another
is convinced that I care
will they listen with interest
to the words I have to share.

7
COURAGE

With this as kindling your cause will ignite.

Warriors that are led by a captain with valor can alter the outcome of a battle thought lost. Armies that assemble behind a general who is fearless will drive larger forces from the field into the sea. And a king that stands unafraid when besieged will inspire and bind a nation to his side. Courage in battle, regardless of the cause, is required of the leader who endeavors to succeed.

Though your call may not demand risk of life nor of limb you must lead with courage as if it were so. Today you must confront that which you fear; for if you are to lead with confidence and courage you must conquer the foes which have thus faced you down.

And who are the opponents that must be vanquished before you can lead with valor and distinction? If you are like most, procrastination, fear of failure and fear of other's opinion are the enemies which have caused you to waver when their path has intersected at the point of your own. But in fear of these foes you will no longer tremble, if today you will face them and turn them away.

Procrastination, which is simply the great fear of beginning, must be the first of your fears to be conquered. Unique among the foes which dwell within your mind, procrastination does not attempt to frighten you with its power or scare you with its weaponry. On the contrary, it actually *encourages* you to begin those endeavors which cause you apprehension. "By all means, confront that which frightens you," it says, "but" (and herein lies the secret to its power), "*wait until tomorrow*, when conditions will surely be more favorable."

This fear and subsequent postponement of beginning will effectively neutralize those who are weak and must be overcome if you are to advance. There is but one perfect moment to confront this fear - and that is now.

Procrastination is the most suppressing of your foes, thus its defeat shall require an arsenal which is equal to its challenge. Your maker has graciously enlisted within your spirit a powerful ally to combat the paralyzing effects of this fear - and it is ACTION. As water is to a flame, so too is action to your fear: they are of opposing constitution and cannot coincide. Henceforth, call upon action when confronted with procrastination and it shall be overcome.

Begin at once by planting three simple words within your mind and repeat them to yourself over and over again. Soon this phrase will indwell within your spirit and you will instinctively obey its command when procrastination tempts you to postpone those things which you know must be done if you are to succeed. *Do it now*. This shall be the battle cry that summons the brave warrior of action. *Do it now*. Repeat these words when the fear of beginning renders you immobile - and you will act. *Do it now*. *Do it now*. And the fear, which is procrastination, will retreat in defeat. Conquer this foe and *do it now*.

Opportunity comes to all,
but success is reserved for the bold.

Has there ever been a time in your life when you sought and were presented with an opportunity that was golden, only to timidly refuse it in the moment of action? If so, there is only one explanation for your lack of courage: *The fear of failure - with its imagined catastrophic outcome - was greater than your desire for success.*

If you are to be counted among the valiant and victorious you must recognize that most fears of failure are irrational and seldom grounded in reality. Rarely will you be called upon to attempt an endeavor where the consequence of life or death hangs in the balance. Likewise, there are few opportunities that, if you were to fail, would require the removal of your loved ones from your home. Therefore, do not allow your fear of failure, with such imagined dire consequences, to prohibit you from attempting a multitude of worthy endeavors.

From this day forth, when presented with an opportunity that is promising, ask yourself the following question:

'What is the worst that shall happen to me
if I attempt this endeavor and fail?'

Shall you lose your life? Probably not. Shall your loved ones be sold in the market as slaves? Again, the answer is most certainly no. When such irrational fears attempt to overwhelm you, simply pause and ponder this question. Upon the realization that no great calamity shall befall you, turn the fear that you have known into faith and instead ask:

'What is the good that shall come my way
if I attempt this endeavor...*and succeed?'*

With newfound boldness as your ally, embrace and attempt the opportunity which beckons. *And you will succeed.*

The final accomplice you must enlist in your battle against fear is CONVICTION; for this is the aide that will strengthen your resolve to stand up for what is right, alone if necessary, in the face of that which is wrong.

In your journey through this life you will observe many leaders who cast their finger to the wind of public opinion when a decision is needed, with nary a thought to principle or conviction. You will notice others who fearfully bow to pressure from one group or another when their position is challenged or when threatened with loss of support.

Sadly, these timid souls have no strength behind their beliefs and are easily intimidated by the forceful reasoning of others. Soon, their influence will be rendered nil by their lack of conviction and their fear of other's opinion.

How often have you expressed your beliefs with great courage when the battlefield was empty, only to retreat in fear when the mighty foes of pressure or conflicting opinion appeared on the horizon?

Let this be no more. Today, put away your timidity at once and for all, summon the courage which comes only with conviction and stand upon principle when coerced or opposed.

Principle is to be prized above popularity.

With conviction, likewise take to task the status quo whose traditions are tired and in need of revision. No longer must you fear that your suggestion of change bestow upon you the mantle of unpopularity. Henceforth, if change is needed stand with conviction and propose the change. In like manner, no longer sit timidly in silence while the forceful words of the majority go unchallenged when you know them to be untrue. If truth is needed you must speak with conviction and challenge the untruth.

This and every day carry with bravery the banner for that which is right, regardless of personal cost or benefit. And though the immediate consequence of your courage be not to your favor, trust in the trueness of your maker's ledger and that your account shall be credited in due time.

From this day forth stand with conviction for the cause you hold dear. Boldly confront that which you fear; and act.

And courage, which is contagious, will spread throughout your ranks.

COURAGE

~

A man once moved
from the land he had known
in search of a village
to live and call his own.
But the village he chose,
chose to greet him with hate,
for it seems he was different -
and they were afraid.

His customs were unlike
the ones that they knew;
his skin, also different
from theirs in its hue.
Yet his heart was the same,
but to this they were blind;
for the heart can't be seen
through a closed, narrow mind.

I stumbled upon
this injustice one day
and was led to address it,
'fore going my way.
For wrong only grows
if ignored and unchecked,
lest those who are brave
take a stand to correct.

I challenged my friends
to battle this foe,
but most were unmoved
to fight status quo.
I then asked my maker,
"Just what should I do?"
He said, *"Start where you are,
I'll draw them to you."*

So the problem I faced
tho' alone and with fear,
yet within a short time
a few gathered near.
We met with the man
and were moved by his plight;
now his cause we've joined
and together we fight.

Soon many more
joined our noble campaign;
our numbers grew strong,
momentum we gained.
From the front did I lead -
and not from the rear;
this wrong would be conquered,
and with it, my fear.

We battled the foe
and our confidence grew,
while those who opposed us
eventually withdrew.

And now there's an army
that spreads 'cross the land
all because of the few
who had taken a stand.

For fear is no match
to those with a cause,
who bravely confront
and press on without pause.
So to those who would lead,
stand up for what's right...
with courage as kindling,
your cause will ignite.

8
ASSOCIATION

—— ❦ ——

Those who journey with the wise shall likewise become;
and a companion of mediocrity, the same.

Set before you at the age of accountability was the power to determine your course. Many choices, factors and decisions have thus far crossed your path, each with its own level of influence on the outcome of your life. But there is one factor that influences your fate more than all others, and that is the great law of association. Simply stated, *you will become liken to those with whom you journey.*

Can a man walk with his companions through a fire and not be burned? No more than a herd pass through the stream and one remain dry. Such is the power of the law of association.

Far too many journey with the masses, traveling aimlessly with those who've traded opportunity for security, and challenge for a life of ease. This mentality of mediocrity has permeated their being and thus, they've become. If the steps of your life have led you down this path, depart today from the meandering of the mediocre herds and join with a caravan which journeys toward success.

As iron sharpens iron, so too does one mind
challenge another and thus, become stronger.

From this day forward surround yourself with confidants who share your quest for growth; for you will challenge them, and they, you - and together you will grow.

You must recognize, however, that many within your current circle will not share your desire for challenge and change. What, then, shall you do when your paths must be linked for a season? Accept them with understanding, yet encourage them to expand their horizon; for were you not once constrained in the camp of contentment as they are? As the burning coal ignites the cold one beside it, so too shall your zeal rekindle the dreams of others. In such manner shall their fire be fueled and blaze with the one you've begun.

Hasten to where the prosperous gather - and listen.

The path on which you journey has been traveled by many who have flourished; and of these, many overflow with knowledge and desire to share it. If prosperity is your goal, seek counsel with those who've excelled in your calling that you might partake of their wisdom and learn of their ways.

How, though, will this be accomplished if you have not yet achieved significant stature to insert yourself into their sphere of influence?

Simply transport yourself to the places where they gather - and be liken to the sponge. Absorb the waters of their wisdom and in due time you shall be filled with the same. Humbly listen to their words and assimilate their knowledge, so that you too, may prosper as they have. And though it cost you in gold and in time, be not concerned; for the knowledge that you will gain will repay your investment a hundred, nay a thousand-fold.

Furthermore, single out a leader in your field who has prospered and whose character is worthy of your followship. Glean from their example and pattern your success after theirs. And though the outward appearance of their prosperity be apparent to all, be more influenced by the inner character which shows forth in their deeds. Covet not what they *have*, but aspire to what they *have become*. Follow in the steps of a leader who is wise, and likewise you will become.

While traveling on the road to success,
decline all directions from those who've not yet departed.

As you journey you must be careful to limit your association with those who know not of what they speak. If you seek to earn ten measures of gold per year, whose instruction should you heed? The one who earns ten or the one who earns two? Heed the words of the one who earns ten; for the one who earns two - though he speak with authority and sincerity - does not know how.

When tempted to fall sway to their persuasive yet empty speech, treat their words as a tongue which you do not understand and banish its sounds from your ears. Seek instead the counsel of those who have achieved the goal for which you strive; for in all matters, the words of one who has prospered are far weightier than the words of one who has not.

A mind, once embarked upon the journey to wisdom,
seldom returns to the thinking of its past.

Finally, as you begin to understand this law of association and its power you must also apply it to the written word that you allow into your mind. The mind is a storehouse with great capacity, but is often filled with dubious knowledge and meaningless trivialities. In truth, much of this - though at times interesting and entertaining - is of insignificant value.

Henceforth, monitor closely the words which you allow to congregate within your mind. Balance the interesting and entertaining with a heavier dose of wisdom and use these words to challenge your thinking, improve your skills and enhance your station in life.

Take special notice of the scrolls of wisdom which have passed through the ages; for like wise counsel, they are available for your benefit if you seek them with sincerity. Dwell among these writings and read them to your advantage; for, though the author may long be departed, in such way shall you learn from his words as if he were here.

From this day forth associate with the words and ways of leaders who are wise....and likewise, you shall become.

THE PARABLE OF ASSOCIATION
~

This is a tale of three young men
who set a course to lead;
each was influenced by his peers
and soon their ways did heed.
For it seems there's a principle
that dictates whom we'll be;
more than birth, more than heritage,
even more than deeds.
This law is set in stone -
full of truth, 'ever sturdy -
and says that we'll become
just like those with whom we journey.
So choose your counsel wisely,
for this has much to say
with whom you will become
when tomorrow is today.

The first young man convinced himself
a title was the key
to make the masses follow him,
and thus a leader be.
Foolishly he chose
only friends of similar mind:
namely those who sought prestige
and an honored place in line.
Like those within his circle
he was soon obsessed with status;
and like them, walked with haughty pride
when on the streets he passed.

To be sure, some respect
his position did bestow,
but most saw right through him
for the falseness of his goal.
Although he had risen
to a title of renown,
the Proverb of Association
served to bring him down.
For it seems he'd been influenced
by those within his sphere,
pursuing and consumed
by the status they held dear.

And when his days were dwindling
and his title was no more,
the masses had no reason
to regard him as before.
He'd become like his companions,
never earning true respect;
goodwill he'd never shown,
and compassion, did neglect.
Thus he traveled to his grave,
a failure 'ever more;
like his friends, only seeking
the title on his door.

The next young man surmised
that wealth would bring acclaim,
so he sought friends with gold
to enhance his humble name.

What he did not understand
is that gold is but a source
to secure material items,
and respect, it cannot force.
Nonetheless, he endeavored,
and much wealth did acquire;
and soon he was accepted
in the circles he desired.

But instead of seeking those
who had wisdom with their wealth,
he sought others like him
only interested in self.
For show, they gave to charity,
(but in the public square)
to be certain others saw them
when their gold they chose to share.
By their ways he was influenced,
and like them, soon became;
treating those with less than him
with rudeness and disdain.

Then sadly, in the end,
all his gold disappeared;
and likewise did the so-called friends
whose ways he had revered.
Influenced by their wealth,
he had failed the greatest test
and not invested in those things
which bring true happiness.

He'd pushed away his loved ones
and become just like his friends;
on a lifelong search for gold,
finding nothing in the end.

The third man took a different route
and sought not friends with things;
for wisely did he understand
respect, these cannot bring.
Instead he chose to congregate
with those who had pure heart,
in hopes that he might gather
of the wisdom they'd impart.
As he watched and observed,
the leaders, he perceived,
were the ones who served without regard
for what they might receive.

So he chose of them to be a friend
and learn their noble traits;
he'd join them as they humbly served,
their ways, he'd emulate.
He walked with them at length,
and in time, their ways obtained,
and like them, did he earn respect
and thus, influence gain.
Through the power of this Proverb
and its law had he succumbed:
because he walked with those who led,
a leader he'd become.

He'd stumbled upon a principle
that is no mystery;
for it seems with whom we walk
thus determines whom we'll be.
For good or for bad,
we'll accumulate the traits
of those with whom we journey
and elect to congregate.
So if you seek to prosper,
learn this truth and make it known:
choose companions wisely,
for their ways will be your own.

9
EXAMPLE

—— ⚉ ——

*Example is the only currency
which buys lasting commitment.*

Though a visionary's effort is the platform from which all great movements are launched, there has never been a cause which was carried to its completion solely on the back of its leader. Likewise, there is no record of a general who defeated his foes while his troops stood idly by. And never has a king single-handedly repelled the conquering armada of his counterpart while his own ships remained in the harbor.

History tells us that solitary success on the grand scale is unachievable, *for nothing great has ever been accomplished alone.* The triumphs which are recalled for a thousand years occur only when a courageous leader and the inspired masses come together in a cause which is larger than either. And so shall it be with the venture you've embraced. Though your heart bursts with passion for a purpose which is noble, your visions of success are in vain lest others are inspired to join the cause for which you toil. How, then, shall you gain the influence which inspires others to action?

Shall it be by the eloquence of your speech? No; for many have ability to stir their audience with emotion but lack the power of lasting persuasion. Shall you entice them with riches? Likewise no; for loyalty purchased by promise of land or loot shall fade when the rivers of reward cease to flow. Shall you harness their help by force?

Most certainly no; for countless others have coerced their charges to comply under threat of the gallows, only to see its rope around their own neck when the winds of rebellion stirred the air.

Be grateful that you have not gold nor land nor the strength of hand to compel others to your cause, for the cooperation secured by such things is temporary and will not last. The source of enduring influence lies not in your power or passion or promises of pay - but in your EXAMPLE; for 'tis only when you demonstrate the depth of your conviction will others commit to your cause and convert it to their own.

Your writings they may read and forget; your voice they may hear and ignore; *but your deeds they will see and remember.* If your words are to carry weight you must henceforth back them with the force of your example. If your teaching and instruction are to impart with credibility you must demonstrate that which you've done. And if your cause is to attract another to embrace it, they must witness you live its message each day.

The group will go far when the leader goes first.

Never demand another to undertake a task which you find unpleasant; *begin the work and they will be quickened to help.* Neither ask others to walk where you are unwilling to tread; *embark upon the path and they will soon follow.* And above all, never request sacrifice when you have yet to pay the price; *be the first to give and others will be inspired to do the same.*

It is your persistence in the face of rejection that will spur them to press on when the force of discouragement compels them to quit. Likewise shall your feats of resistance to that which is wrong provoke them to stand for that which is right. And your unwavering faith midst the shadows of doubt shall teach them to trust with assurance in the source of all truth.

You have only one command to inspire the action of others, and it is simply thus: *Follow me.* Let this be your cry as you lead your cause and many will heed your call.

THE PARABLE OF EXAMPLE

~

Everyone agreed,
the problem was quite great,
for some within their village
had no food upon their plate.
"Let's see what can be done,"
the so-called leaders did resound;
yet when the time for action came,
they could not be found.
They'd agreed there was a problem,
but their lives it had not reached;
so to their homes they returned
and forgot about the need.
They'd started with great fervor,
but soon it swiftly passed;
for passion without action
quickly fades and cannot last.
Occasionally they'd gather
and themselves congratulate
their grandiose intentions
and their coins within the plate.
But their actions did not match
their pats upon their backs,
for they'd shunned those in need
and turned away from those who lacked.
They went about their lives
and with self, became absorbed,
while the problem in their midst
was neglected and ignored.

"Let someone else address it,"
seemed to be the thought of most;
"besides, I once gave gold,"
was the verse they oft did boast.
But gold was not the answer -
nor the greatest need;
what was needed was for someone
to step forth and take the lead.
All the while the problem grew
and refused to go away;
while those with power to help
chose to look the other way.

Then one day, one among them
made the choice to take a stand;
alone, she faced the problem
and began to lend a hand.
Her talents were not many,
no great things had she attained;
but because of her example
great respect she soon had gained.
By her willingness to act
those in need knew she cared,
and others from her circle
were compelled to give and share.
When they witnessed her example
they aspired to be a part
of the movement she had started
with compassion in her heart.

They gathered up the excess
of their gold and of their bread,
and shared with those among them
whom before, they had misread.
And soon the total village
was involved within the need,
all because one among them
made the choice to take the lead.
She understood this Proverb
and its principle, did prove:
for 'tis only when you lead the charge
will others follow you.
So if you face a challenge
where the work is unbegun,
initiate the action...
and a leader you'll become.

▣

10
PERSPECTIVE

———— ✺ ————

From the vantage point of the eternal
only the important is exposed.

Like the shaking of the earth the challenges of life are beyond your control and often arrive without warning or notice, while a measure of suffering, setback, discouragement and defeat is promised to the plate of all and thusly apportioned at the allotted time.

For many, when such hardship has joined with their journey they beg pitifully for reprieve from its pain, seeing only its difficulty and never its design. For others, when trials and trouble appear on their trail they flee in great fear and refuse to press on. But a few know these fires have been sent to refine them, and endure them to emerge emblazoned with strength. By what means or method do they brave the furnace, while most others wilt in the heat of lesser flames? The answer is PERSPECTIVE: the strong view their trials from the height of the greater good; while the weak, from the shallow depths of their discomfort.

Were you to walk alone on the sojourn of life a narrow field of vision would surely suffice: but you do not, for others now look to you for guidance and direction. What must you do to elevate your view when your feet become mired in the soil of misfortune? Only one force shall boost you to the point of clarity when answers and discernment have fled from your midst: and it is your attitude. Henceforth, pose one simple question when faced with a setback, for its utterance is as wind to the eagle's wings and will lift your point of view to the ridge of understanding. Its words are simply thus:

'What treasure has arrived disguised as this trial?'

No longer must you cower in fear when adversity appears as an enemy at your door, for perhaps it was sent that you might sharpen your skill. Neither moan the loss if desertion should reduce your troops to near nothing, for perchance it paid visit to sift the weak from your ranks. And waste not a word lamenting its delay if success should postpone its visit for a season. Consider that your character was not ready to receive it and embrace the extra time as required to prepare you.

When the voice of resistance to your vision is fervent receive it not as mutiny, but welcome it as a chance to restate your common cause. When the drummers of dissension beat loudly hear them not as insult, but step with them a measure and return them to your march. And when the wayward flames of those who oppose you burn zealous face them without flinching, for the fires of their passion - once rekindled with your own - shall forge you as one.

With your vision unveiled by this elevated view never again will you withdraw in despair down the path of self-pity and curse the challenge which shadows your steps. In the light of the eternal you will seek its true purpose, and rejoice and be grateful when it is revealed.

Though the fog of limited perception has proceeded to lift, still there is much that is shrouded from your sight. How, then, shall you guide yourself and others past the plains of the unclear, through the forest of the unseen and beyond the horizon of the unknown? There is only one answer: *you must walk in the light of the one who sees all*.

For in this lamp, only the important is exposed.

THE PARABLE OF PERSPECTIVE

~

A leader climbed the mountain trail
to leave his trials behind,
for it seems he'd lost perspective
and his bearings, could not find.
His life's work he had started
with vision and with song;
full of joy was his heart -
but now, it was gone.

He felt as though the world
was strapped upon his back,
while the gravity of life
sought to pull him from his track.
As he strolled along the ridge
he paused to reflect
on the path that he had chosen:
had he somehow been misled?

The higher he had risen
seemed the burdens had increased,
and from pressure and adversity
he could not find relief.
He perceived all solutions
on him, did thus depend;
while demands for his time
were at a never seeming end.

Alone on the mountain top
he fretted on his fate

and pondered on the purpose
of the challenges he faced.
And then at once his problems
were reduced in scope and size,
for slowly he began to see
his world with brand new eyes.

The splendor of creation
he'd not noticed for some time,
for his vision had been blinded
by the focus of his climb.
As he marveled at the beauty,
with perspective and with awe,
his maker's handiwork
made his troubles seem so small.

A voice deep within him
whispered gently to his soul,
*"These burdens that you face,
I have them all under control.
I'm the one who made you,
not to mention this whole world;
so do not be concerned
when stones of strife at you are hurled.*

*"And do not be disheartened
when your trials bring you pain,
for someday you will understand
that each was for your gain.
Now go back to your journey
and remember this each day:
keep all things in perspective
and you'll never lose your way."*

Thus he went back to his mission
no longer overwhelmed
by the challenges he faced
at his station at the helm.
Refreshed and renewed,
with a vigor that was new,
from now he vowed to see things
from the larger point of view.

And whenever trials befell him
and their cause was concealed,
to the mountain top he'd climb
for their purpose to reveal.
From this lofted point
would all problems he behold
and watch with admiration
his creator's plan unfold.

So no matter what the burden
or the challenge faced by you,
ascend to the vista
which elevates your view.
For high above the problem
do we see the larger plan.....
and 'tis there we gain perspective
and begin to understand.

11
SERVANTHOOD

— ✍ —

Success will not hide from those who humbly serve.

In this, the final teaching, we return full circle to the premise which began us: *What is the greater purpose to your passage on this earth and for what divine endeavors have your days been designed?*

Are riches and reward the only reason for your toils, or have your talents been entrusted for higher tasks to complete? And why has the leader's book of Proverbs passed to you? Are you to learn its lessons with no goal but to prosper, or shall its wisdom be employed for reasons yet revealed?

Contemplate these questions and the call upon your life and consider if your course is in need of correction. With no greater sense of mission than to prosper and be praised, have your passions propelled you down the trail of empty treasure? Or perhaps you have succumbed to the seduction of success and deceived yourself to deem important what is not?

Although riches and acclaim in great measure may you gain, are these to be the end to which your efforts are directed? Forbid this to be so! - for your life will be for naught if you carry to your grave no greater prizes than these.

How, then, shall you separate from the path of vain pursuits and set upon the road which shall lead to true reward? Start by examining the desires which detour you and ask with indifference the following of each:

'What significance will this hold
when my days are no more?'

Shall a storehouse full of gold carry any currency in the life which is to come? It shall not. Shall the fleeting praise of man for which you strain to fill your ears resound for even a second when you have departed? Likewise, no. The credit of such things shall account for nothing when the ledger of your life is closed. Why, then, should you toil for prestige which is passing or for riches which must remain when fate has removed you? You must not! From this day forth assign to them a measure of effort equal to their importance and wear yourself weary for their attainment no more.

There is only one road which leads to significance, and its steps are the same if a leader you shall be: SERVANTHOOD is the portal through which you must pass; amend your quest now that you might journey through its gate. Today, bring your search for riches to its end....and begin to serve.

It is only when you give with no thought for your gain
will your purpose be revealed, your stature be enhanced
and your life be filled with wealth which is true.

This principle seems peculiar to those who have not practiced it, for its doctrine is at odds with the self-promoting ways which prevail in the land. Be honest, have you not often pondered in doubt and disbelief, "*How is it possible to give what I have and expect to gain more? Won't the resources of my treasury and talent eventually deplete if I serve with no regard for myself?*"

As unexplainable as the origin of the Almighty and as perplexing to comprehend, this law nonetheless worketh without fail: *Give without regard for reward and great gain shall return unto you.* You must no longer question how this principle is so, but in faith begin to test it and its truth will be seen.

Do you desire to increase your standing and esteem? *They will grow to great heights when you step from your platform and quietly serve.* Do you wish gold and riches to abide within your chest? *They will flow in abundance when you labor with the goal that your people prosper first.* And what of joy and enduring satisfaction? *They will flood your soul indeed when you pour of your time and treasure into the lives of those who have no means to repay you.* Success will not hide from one who freely gives, for it hastens to embrace all who humbly serve.

Though this law is proved as truth, what shall be said of those times in your past when it seemeth to have failed, for your giving did not return either riches or respect? If you are honest in your reflection you will likely see that it was you who failed and not this law, for your motives were misguided and your serving, for selfish gain.

Though you gave of your gold to those who had none, did you secretly expect them to return it with interest? Likewise of the food which was shared from your cupboard: Was it to feed those who hungered (or your need to feel noble)? And of the assistance you rendered to those seeking help: Did you do so in secret, or announce it from a stage that you might bask in applause?

So long as you cling to these self-centered ways you will never helm the ship which others seek to follow. Today, depart from this course and begin a new life which is focused on others. Today, put away the selfish ways of your past and remove the lenses which have turned your gaze inward. Today, begin to give without regard for return; for 'tis then, and only then, will significance, stature and lasting fulfillment be granted unto you.

As the teaching of these principles approaches its conclusion it is hoped that the essence of their truths has emerged: *To gain you must give without regard for return. To succeed you must labor that others prosper first. And to lead you must humble yourself to serve.* This is the sum of the knowledge you've received, and you must take it with you as you go forth from here. These are likewise the laws by which the great among us live. Embrace them as your mottos and be counted among them.

Your sojourn upon this soil is brief and rushes headlong toward its end. The memory of your life will soon fade and be forgotten, but the legacy of your giving will live on in those you've led. No longer must you *seek*, but in all things must you *serve* and soon those who follow will likewise do the same.

There is but one purpose to your passage on this earth, and you've begun the journey which will see it come to pass. You are called to lead others to the land of true reward. Take the road of the servant and many will follow.

EPILOGUE

~

I set out to discover
the purpose for my life;
I sought and searched with diligence,
yet only found much strife.
I traveled many roads
and I searched, 'round and 'round;
yet the meaning I was seeking
was nowhere to be found.

I then assumed my labor
would contentment surely bring;
and it seemed to for a season,
but it soon became routine.
I accomplished many things,
they were notched upon my belt;
yet the more that I achieved,
the more alone inside I felt.

Though a leader I'd become,
with great numbers in my charge,
the purpose I was after
was obscured and still at large.
Surrounded by abundance
and outwardly, much blessed,
on the inside I was filled
with enduring emptiness.

I tried to fill the void
with gold and many things,
and convinced myself that these,
would happiness thus bring.
So I purchased and I bought
and collected and acquired,
yet the more that I obtained,
seemed the more that I desired.

My trinkets brought some pleasure
but not true happiness,
and when their newness became old,
once again, back to my quest.
For all my earthly treasures
and the gold within my till
could not fill a space
they were ill-equipped to fill.

I then resigned myself
that my searching was for naught;
for I could not seem to find
the purpose that I sought.
And then one day it happened,
and it all became quite clear;
I discovered life's true meaning
and the reason why we're here.

On a dusty road I traveled
when I heard a cry for help;
in the bushes by the roadside
was a stranger who'd been felled.

It appeared that he was beaten
and in need of helping hand;
but my first thought was to pass him by,
for I knew not this man.

I continued on my journey
yet the quiet voice within
whispered "*Go back to that man
and stop and comfort him.*"
So to the stranger I returned,
unsure of what to do;
but when I saw him in his pain
my compassion for him grew.

I took him to an inn
and the keeper I then paid
for lodging and for food
for as long as he need stay.
As I went back to my journey
tears of joy began to flow,
for I'd found what I'd been seeking,
and the truth, I now did know.

You can strive to be a leader
with influence over all,
but if you seek instead of serve,
you've missed your maker's call.
So waste not a moment
on pursuits that cannot last,
but start to give and what you'll find
is joy that will not pass.

For it seems that life is found
not in what we get -
but at the point we start to serve
is where it will be met.
So to those who search for meaning,
I've but this advice to give:
*"Give without concern for self...
and then you'll start to live."*

The End

About the Author

Stevenson Willis is the founder and leader of youth for truth, a ministry and mentor program which teaches at-risk inner city young people to empower themselves with positive thinking, life goals and the application of Biblically based success principles.

He resides in Nashville, TN and is the author, producer and director of motivationally themed audio-visual materials. His previous work includes the MASTERS OF SELLING Audio Book *As you think it, so shall it be,* and the public broadcasting documentary film *Profiles of the American Dream*, an international bestseller which has been broadcast and distributed in multiple languages worldwide.

Please contact Pillar Press for speaking engagement information.